MIDDLE GRADE ASSESSMENTS

A BOOK OF RUBRICS, CHECKLISTS, AND ASSESSMENTS FOR GRADES 5–8

BY DR. LINDA KARGES-BONE

Dedication and Message

"Teach us to number our days and recognize how few they are: help us to spend them as we should." (Psalm 90:12 TLB) As teachers, we have precious little time to waste as we work to mold and shape young lives. We must remember that the business of assessment and evaluation is sensitive and powerful and that young people's potential will be either encouraged or subdued by our assessment of their work.

This book is dedicated to my colleagues in the School of Education at Charleston Southern University: BJ, Bernadette, Don, Jerry, Joanna, Jon, Marlene, Martha, Nancy, Pat, and Peter. Working with all of you during the past decade has been an inspiration and a privilege.

Acknowledgements

Special thanks to the staff of the Center for Excellence in the Assessment of Student Learning, University of South Carolina at Columbia, for making assessment a priority, not an afterthought, and to the South Carolina Department of Education for its efforts in developing the *Frameworks*, which encourage teachers to think deliberately about curriculum and assessment.

Project Manager: Mina McMullin
Editors: Kathy Zaun, Jill Kaufman
Production and Design: Good Neighbor Press, Inc., Grand Junction, CO
Cover Design: Signature Design Group, Inc.

GOOD APPLE
A Division of Frank Schaffer Publications, Inc.
23740 Hawthorne Blvd.
Torrance, CA 90505

ISBN 0-7682-0011-3

TABLE OF CONTENTS

ABOUT THIS BOOK

Dear Middle Grade Teachers,

If you are reading this letter, you probably belong to one of two groups of middle grade teachers: those who couldn't find a job in the lower or higher grades, or that larger, much happier group of teachers who absolutely love middle school. I'm not joking. After more than a decade of preparing future teachers at the university, I am certain of one thing: middle school teachers are born, not made.

It never ceases to amaze me, the epiphany that occurs when a future teacher who "always wanted to teach little children" discovers the magic of middle school. He or she recognizes the unique wit of the seventh-grader; responds to the curiosity of the sixth-grader; or identifies with the angst of the eighth-grader. These teachers typically approach their middle school clinical experience as if it is a landmine and leave it vowing that middle school is a goldmine filled with treasure.

If you love teaching middle grades, then you will probably like *Middle Grade Assessments* for two reasons. First, it will free up your time. Middle grade teachers have no time to waste. Keeping up with the young adolescent is a rigorous task. Team meetings, conferences with parents (whose middle school kids are making them middle-aged quickly), and the serious business of planning for the more advanced content of middle school can leave even the most polished professional exhausted. Second, you will like this book because it deals with the topic that many teachers (at all grade levels) avoid—assessment. Although research indicates that teachers spend up to 40% of their time doing assessment, my doctoral studies suggest that fewer than 20% of teachers had a course in designing assessment during undergraduate school.

I have found that for most teachers, assessment and evaluation are "learn as you go" areas of expertise. Most teachers report that they learn about assessment from 1) experience, 2) watching and borrowing from mentor teachers, and 3) pursuing books and workshops on their own. That brings us to this point. You probably picked up *Middle Grade Assessments* because you want to know more about "How to do assessment." Congratulations! You found some wonderful and very useful information.

Included in this book are reproducible rubrics, checklists, and assessment tools that are designed to be generic. You can plug in the content yourself. It is the students' handling of the content, processing of the information, and synthesis of the material into a new product that can be evaluated and reported on.

Moreover, simple instructions have been provided to move you into designing your own assessment tools when you feel ready or have a unique need. Perhaps most helpful will be the *Glossary of Assessment Terms* (pages 104–106) and the time line team planning questions (page 111). Teams of teachers are important at the middle school level, and if assessment is going to be done across a team, you must plan ahead for how and when that will occur.

Finally, *Middle Grade Assessments* includes reproducible parent postcards in the Appendix (pages 107–108) that you can send home to keep parents involved. Parent communication and cooperation are always important, but in the difficult, shifting middle school years, both are critical. Parents often feel disconnected from the middle school. It seems colder and more distant than the friendly, approachable elementary school. Don't let that happen in your school. Use parent letters and other tools to help parents keep up with student progress and also to help parents feel wanted and needed by you!

Middle Grade Assessments is a perfect way to ease confusion about assessment and make it more relevant and meaningful for your students.

Linda Karges-Bone, Ed.D.

INTRODUCTION

WHAT'S SO MARVELOUS ABOUT MIDDLE SCHOOL?

Something to Think About:
"The attempt and not the deed confounds us."
(William Shakespeare in Macbeth)

◆◆

Middle Grade Assessments is filled with a variety of ways for you to assess students' work. Reproducible rubrics, checklists, and assessment tasks are just a few of the items contained in this book. To better familiarize yourself with the contents of this book, apples and outlines of students have been included on the top right corner of many pages to help you determine which pages have been designed for teachers (🍎) and which have been designed for students (🧑). Teacher-directed pages can be used for assessment or evaluation. The pages containing student outlines are student-directed pages. These can be used for review, for checkpoints, for enrichment, for remediation, or to send home for homework or parent communication.

Materials in the Introduction and How to Use Them

Below is a list of information found on the next several pages that will enable you to begin to learn how to start assessing.

◆ Page 9 will help you tighten up your expectations for giving assessment. The information provided will help you think about when and how to do assessment effectively.

◆ The *Assessment Schedule* on page 10 can be used to keep students and their parents informed about when projects are due and tests will be given.

◆ The *Chapter or Theme Outline Form* on page 14 can be used to help students organize information and ideas to prepare for tests.

What Do We Know About the Middle School Student?

The information below about middle school students in general can provide helpful insight when planning methods of assessment.

Middle school students . . .

◆ are interested in "fitting in" with their peer group

◆ are often disorganized and distracted

◆ experience periods of rapid physical growth and change

◆ are beginning to separate emotionally from the family unit

◆ may be strongly interested in the opposite sex

◆ use clothes and jewelry to "make a statement"

◆ think about "this minute" not "next week"

◆ like humor and jokes

◆ may be emotional and very sensitive

◆ are each developing a sense of "who I am" and "who I want to become"

◆ like to work with groups, if they get to "choose their groups"

◆ need to develop an understanding and tolerance of those who are different

◆ may be harsh, critical, or unkind to other students

◆ test boundaries and may challenge adults

SETTING UP AN ASSESSMENT-FRIENDLY CLASSROOM

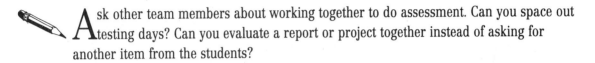

If you want assessment to be an integral, practical part of your classroom routine, then you must plan ahead. Below are some tips to help you do this.

Ask other team members about working together to do assessment. Can you space out testing days? Can you evaluate a report or project together instead of asking for another item from the students?

Set up a container of some sort (bin, basket, portfolio) in which to collect students' work. Always keep students' work in the same place. Middle grade students need routine in order to be successful.

Set due dates for projects, reports, and tests well ahead of time and make sure students have their information in writing.

Expect that middle grade students will forget or procrastinate when it comes to projects. Eliminate the excuses by reminding students daily about upcoming projects.

Settle anxieties about assessment by displaying or pointing out examples of exemplary work. Students at this age are anxious about success and may have confidence problems. They want and need to see what you want from them.

Set aside time during each period to talk about assessment. Ask students about their progress on projects. Provide time for students to peer-review work in progress.

Make a habit of showing students the rubric or checklist you plan to use for a particular test, project, etc., ahead of time. Let them know exactly what you expect from their work.

Experiment with a "half-time" period during testing. Give students three minutes to talk about anything they want during the middle of a test. They cannot look at notes, but they can talk to one another. This helps students "jar their memories" about things they really know yet might be worried or a little confused about.

Note that both traditional (tests) and authentic (tasks) assessments are important and valuable. A balance is what you and the students want and need.

Try giving students peppermint or wintergreen candies to suck on during a test or assignment. The scent and taste encourage alertness and memory.

WHY DO ASSESSMENT?

Before you encounter the many examples of rubrics, checklists, and tasks found on the pages ahead, spend a few minutes reviewing why assessment is done in the first place. A good teacher knows why he or she is evaluating students' work. It isn't about grading, although grades continue to be a compelling force in middle schools. Assessment is more complex than just grades.

Assessment is done to ensure
MASTERY OF THE CONTENT.

Assessment is done to find out
WHAT STUDENTS HAVE LEARNED.

Assessment is done to find out
WHERE TO GO NEXT IN THE CURRICULUM.

Assessment is done to evaluate our own success in
DELIVERING INSTRUCTION.

Assessment is done to
PLAN FOR REMEDIATION OR ENRICHMENT
for students.

Assessment is done for the purpose of
ACCOUNTABILITY TO PARENTS AND COMMUNITY.

❖❖ **REMEMBER:** The purpose of your assessment will guide you in designing the appropriate assessment.

❖❖ **REMEMBER:** Both traditional testing and more authentic forms of assessment can tell you a lot about students. To find out more about the balance between traditional and authentic testing, read *Authentic Instruction and Assessment*, also a Good Apple book.

WHEN IS IT TIME TO DO ASSESSMENT?

The timing of assessment is critical. You want to do an assessment when you have covered enough material, but before you overwhelm students with content. It takes good planning in order to be fair and effective. Below are some guidelines.

◆ Develop a Long-Range Plan (LRP) for your quarter or semester. Decide ahead of time how far you plan to go in a textbook, with a theme, or through a set of curriculum objectives. Write this down or use a calendar to make the task visual and clear.

◆ Set "Assessment Checkpoints" on your LRP. For example, in mathematics, perhaps the chapter on fractions is a tough one for your students. Decide ahead of time to divide the chapter into two parts and to give two assessments. Perhaps you will do a traditional "test" with one part (sets of problems) and then try a more authentic "task" with the rest of the material. This gives the students a more manageable piece of content to digest and also offers appropriate ways for them to use their learning styles and talents to demonstrate their knowledge.

◆ Never plan for a test on a Monday. The students will not study over the weekend. Use Monday as a pre-test or review day. Test on Tuesday instead.

◆ Consider sending home an "Assessment Schedule" for the month. If possible, make this a team effort. This form will help keep students and parents informed about when projects are due and tests will be given. A sample form has been included for you to use, as well as an example. (See pages 10 and 11.)

◆ Individual student differences must be addressed in the timing of assessments. Students who have attention problems or learning disabilities should be assessed in smaller, more frequent events. This helps them feel more organized and more successful.

Always do a thorough review prior to the assessment. Perhaps give students a study guide to assist visual learners and parents. There's nothing like a parent driving a sixth-grader to school in the morning with the study guide in one hand and a mug of coffee in the other (plus a steering wheel) while he or she rattles off questions for the chapter test!

ASSESSMENT SCHEDULE

Team_____ Teacher_____ Subject _____

Grade Level_____ Duration _____

Test Date _____ Chapters_____

Test Date _____ Chapters_____

Test Date _____ Chapters_____

Test Date _____ Chapters_____

Project Due Date _____

Notes on Project _____

_____

Project Due Date _____

Notes on Project _____

_____

Report Due Date _____

Criteria for Report _____

_____

_____

Reading Assignments _____

Due Dates _____

SAMPLE ASSESSMENT SCHEDULE

Team _The Rockets_   Teacher _Mr. Rodriguez_   Subject _Language Arts_

Grade Level _6th_   Duration _September_

Test Date _Sept. 6th_   Chapters _Ch. 2 on "Myths and Legends"_

Test Date _Sept. 20th_   Chapters _Ch. 2 on "Tall Tales"_

Test Date _Sept. 25th_   Chapters _Vocabulary Test_

Test Date _____ Chapters _____

Project Due Date _Sept. 12th_

Notes on Project _Creative Story on "Your Own Tall Tale" is due. Minimum of 4 pages handwritten or 2 pages typed._

Project Due Date _____

Notes on Project _____

Report Due Date _Sept. 30th_

Criteria for Report _Use the Internet to research 2 sites: one on the Loch Ness Monster and one on Big Foot. Write one page about how myths and reality clash. Use geography information. This grade is for social studies and language arts._

Reading Assignments _Select book for pleasure reading on monsters or myths._

Due Dates _none_

HOW DO WE DO ASSESSMENT IN MIDDLE SCHOOL?

Can there ever be "too many A's" in middle school? Writing in the journal *Schools in the Middle*, an NASSP publication devoted to the curriculum and culture of middle schools (Sept. 1997), Leslie Kaplan suggests that middle school students can benefit more from an "assessment culture" rather than a "testing culture." This idea fits nicely with the developmental and social needs of youngsters ages 11–15. Students of this age need to learn to organize themselves and to be disciplined. Yet, they need to use assessment to grow, not to be punished. The cycle of "Teach-Test-Grade and Move On" does not offer most middle grade students adequate time for mastery.

In order to ensure mastery, which is the biggest reason for assessment, teachers might implement some of the suggestions put forth by Candy and Hotchkiss (1989) as cited in Dr. Kaplan's article. Three of my favorites include these:

◆ Permitting students to drop their lowest grade or to retake one test during a marking period

◆ Averaging students' grades without assigning zeros for missed homework or late work

◆ Assigning grades only after corrective feedback has been given

USING THE ASSESSMENT MATERIALS IN THIS BOOK FOR MASTERY LEARNING

Below are suggestions to help students achieve mastery learning.

◆ Use a rubric or checklist as a "pre-test". Give an assignment and let students do a "dry run" using the rubric or checklist as their own evaluation tool. Let them evaluate their own work first and then make corrections or revisions before you do a formal evaluation.

◆ Alternate individual assignments with cooperative group assignments. Consider cooperative learning judiciously. It is a good way to help lower-achieving students model the organizational and critical thinking behaviors of higher-achieving students. It can also help "dreamers" stay on-task as the group pushes them to move forward. Use a rubric, checklist, or task as a group assessment one week and then as an individual assessment the next week.

◆ Show students how to outline chapters and material before they use that material for an authentic task or before they are tested on that material. Middle grade students need to practice weeding out content and focusing on critical facts. This is a process that takes months, not weeks.

◆ Avoid the practice of having students copy notes from a board or overhead transparency. This is a handwriting assignment, not a productive study skill. Better mastery-learning choices are as follows:

• Do a chapter outline together to help prepare for assessment. (See form provided on page 14. Make as many copies of it as needed for students to keep in their notebooks.)

• Use copies of authentic materials or novels whenever possible and show students how to use highlighting pens to mark important passages.

• Have students keep "key vocabulary" notebooks. Make a matching bulletin board in each class. Using vocabulary words frequently and appropriately builds mastery.

Name _____ Date _____

CHAPTER OR THEME OUTLINE FORM

• •

Chapter_____ Textbook_____ Theme_____

List key vocabulary words below. Put definitions in a key vocabulary notebook for reference.

_____ _____ _____ _____

_____ _____ _____ _____

_____ _____ _____ _____

_____ _____ _____ _____

List critical concepts below. Note page numbers or sources where references can be found. These concepts will be on the test or assessment.

_____

_____

_____

_____

_____

_____

List supporting concepts below. These ideas or facts support the key concepts and add detail.

_____

_____

_____

_____

_____

_____

_____

_____

_____

_____

CHAPTER ONE
ASSESSMENT IN LANGUAGE ARTS

INTRODUCTION

Something to Think About:
"He said true things, but called them by wrong names."
(Elizabeth Barret Browning)

Assessment in language arts in the middle grades has two goals. First, teachers must demonstrate to the young adolescent exactly what is expected in the written or oral language assessment. Middle school youngsters crave structure, even though they appear to be (and often are) pushing away from adult restraints. They need to know what they need to know.

Second, middle school youngsters need opportunities to demonstrate their abilities in language arts in fair, concise, varied ways. One thing good teachers of middle school students learn about their students is to take their frequent mood swings in stride. One day can be a disaster, and the next day can be "perfect." You had just better hope that your test or task is planned for the brighter day. One way to address this issue, which is developmental and not necessarily a form of punishment meant for teachers, is to plan for a variety of assessment checkpoints during the grading period. In a typical language arts class, a variety might be similar to the following:

Week One: Writing sample and short quiz on grammar; begin novel

Week Two: Oral recitation of a poem

Week Three: Narrative writing assignment and short novel quiz

Week Four: Literature Test (on the novel)

Materials in Chapter One and How to Use Them

This chapter on assessment in language arts comes first in this book because language, both written and oral, is the vehicle by which we deliver information. Students must be able to communicate effectively in all subject areas and in life.

This chapter offers both teacher-directed assessments and student-driven checkpoints and activities to help students prepare for assessments. Remember, you will find either an apple or an outline of students at the top right corner of each reproducible page. These symbols, with the help of the introductory pages in each chapter, will assist you in selecting materials for students to practice with or for you to use as evaluation tools.

The pages listed below provide students opportunities in preparing for assessment. Use these pages for review, as overhead transparencies in instruction, or to allow students to pre-check their own work before a formal assessment.

◆ *Student Checklist for Narrative Writing* (page 18)
◆ *The Conflict Questionnaire* (page 19)
◆ *Checklist for Writing Dialogue* (page 20)
◆ *Research Skills Assessment* (page 23) and *Pre-Research Task Analysis* (pages 25–26)
◆ *Student Pre-Check for Expository Writing Task* (page 27)
◆ *Advertisment Analysis* (page 33)
◆ *Did You Convince Your Reader?* (page 34)
◆ *Proofreading Checklist for Language Arts* (pages 36–38)

The pages listed below are for teachers to use in doing formal assessment of students' work. Each rubric or checklist can stand alone, or the points can be transferred to a traditional grading scale. For example, on a 3-point rubric—3 points might be an A, 2 points might be a B, and 1 point might be a C.

◆ *Rubric for a Narrative Writing Product* (page 21)
◆ *A 3-Point Rubric for Expository Writing* (page 28)
◆ *Checklist for Technical Writing* (page 30)
◆ *A Postcard Assessment for a Business Letter* (page 31)
◆ *Rubric for Persuasive Writing* (page 35)

This chapter is divided into four sections—narrative writing, expository writing, technical writing, and persuasive writing. Each section is explained and contains student activity pages along with teacher pages.

At the end of the chapter is a *Proofreading Checklist for Language Arts* (pages 36–38). Give each student a copy of the checklist to use to evaluate his or her writing tasks.

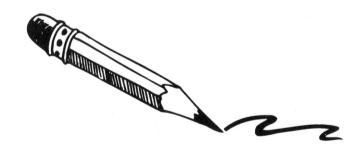

NARRATIVE WRITING IN THE MIDDLE GRADES

Middle grade students are natural narrators. Consider one student's ability to retell a story five different times between the changing of classes and then record a detailed description of the saga of "Alicia and Tom's Break-up" in a note to a friend while you are attempting to teach the concept of "writing dialogue". Oh yes, young teens can actively engage in narrative, but can they put it on paper? That's a different challenge.

Narrative writing includes the writing or retelling of stories, and students must receive instruction in each of the eight components listed below before you attempt to assess narrative writing:

   Story Structure (Every story has a beginning, middle, and ending.)

   Designing and Analyzing Plot (a sequence of events in the story)

   Story Setting (where and when the story unfolds)

   Characters (the look, attitudes, beliefs, and behaviors of the characters)

   Conflict (What problem or issue do the characters confront?)

   Theme (What is the meaning of the story?)

   Writing Dialogue (How do the characters convey their message?)

   Point of View (How does the writer tell the story?)

Have students complete pages 18–20 before you assess them on narrative writing. These pages can be used as a pre-assessment and can help students revise and refine their products before they are evaluated. Then as assessment, give each student a copy of page 21, *Rubric for a Narrative Writing Product*. You can assign points as needed in your grading scale, or use 3–2–1.

Name _____ Date _____

STUDENT CHECKLIST FOR NARRATIVE WRITING

Story Structure

Fill in each box with a brief description of each part of your story.

Box 1	Box 2	Box 3
Beginning	**Middle**	**Ending**

Start with a "theme." Write your theme, or the meaning of your story, inside this box.

Characters Count

Fill in the matrix with information about your main characters.

Names of Characters				
Qualities				
Looks Like				
Talks Like				
Acts Like				

THE CONFLICT QUESTIONNAIRE

1. Can you describe the main problem or problems that your characters encounter?

   _____

2. Do your characters have an inner conflict or an external conflict? Do they have a personal problem or a problem with another individual?

   _____

3. Does the conflict involve nature or the environment? Is a storm, an earthquake, an illness, or an animal the cause of the problem?

   _____

4. Does the conflict focus on a character who has trouble with the rules or expectations of his or her culture or the society in which he or she lives?

   _____

5. Does the conflict center on an issue between characters? Perhaps it is a family conflict or a friendship gone bad. Or, maybe an enemy or a personal threat is the cause of the conflict.

   _____

   ❖❖ **Note:** Remember that conflict can occur at different levels, but in beginning narrative, less is more. It is usually more powerful to develop one kind of conflict in a story and let your characters really go for it!

Setting Up Your Story

Fill in this outline with phrases describing the place or places in which your story develops.

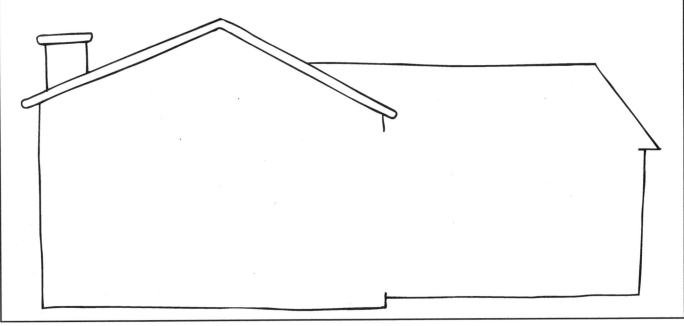

CHECKLIST FOR WRITING DIALOGUE

Did you place quotation marks before and after direct quotations?	Yes	No
Does each quotation make sense?	Yes	No
Does your dialogue sound natural, as if the characters are really talking?	Yes	No
Is it clear to the reader who is speaking? Example: *Juan said, "I'm too tired to play soccer."*	Yes	No
Do you have too much or too little dialogue?	Yes	No
Did you end each quotation with a mark of punctuation?	Yes	No
Was the mark of punctuation appropriate? (question mark/period/exclamation point)	Yes	No
Do you use dialogue to lead the reader into a conflict or resolution in the story?	Yes	No

RUBRIC FOR A NARRATIVE WRITING PRODUCT

Student _____ Date _____

A Well-Written Narrative Product _____ Points _____ Letter Grade

This narrative product tells a story in a meaningful, interesting way. The writer's spelling, grammar, and use of punctuation are correct and add to the readability of the narrative. There are fewer than two simple grammar or spelling errors in the narrative. The characters are well developed in this narrative. The reader understands who they are and what they are about. The dialogue that these characters exchange is clear and written in a way that makes the story easy to follow. The story has a clearly defined beginning, middle, and ending. The conflict or conflicts are understandable and realistic. The reader can easily identify the issues or problems facing these characters. In this narrative, the setting is well developed. The reader can "see" how the setting contributes to the characters and to the conflict. The plot moves logically and realistically, in an organized and timely manner. There is an explicit theme to this story. The reader knows easily what the writer really means.

An Acceptable Narrative Product _____ Points _____ Letter Grade

This narrative product has all the essential parts of a story: a beginning, middle, and ending. The story is told, but the writer might find ways to make it more lively or interesting. There are three to five minor errors in spelling, grammar, or punctuation, but these can be easily corrected. There are no serious internal problems. The characters in this story make sense but could be more fully developed, with details about their motivation or appearance. The dialogue is in place, and it does the job of communicating what the characters have to say. The conflict might be stronger. How do the characters deal with their problems? Could the writer be more clear about the nature of the conflict? The setting is in place, and it adequately describes the time, location, and background of the story. This story has a theme.

An Unacceptable Narrative Product _____ Points _____ Letter Grade

This narrative product tells a story, but it may not hold the reader's interest. The writer's spelling, grammar, and use of punctuation need more refinement. There are more than five simple errors, and there is one or more critical errors (example: a sentence fragment) or a consistent internal problem (example: a problem with subject-verb agreement). This makes the story harder to follow. The characters are developed but perhaps not clearly. It may be hard to pick out the main character or to understand the motivations of the character. This story probably does not have a clearly developed beginning, middle, and ending, and the sequence of events may be confusing at times. The conflict in this narrative may be hard to see, or there may be too many conflicts competing for the reader's attention. The setting is adequate, but the writer might be able to make better use of setting to move the story along or to develop characterization. The plot in this story "jumps around" or is not logical. This story probably does not contain a theme that the reader can recognize or identify with.

Comments: _____

_____

_____

_____

_____

EXPOSITORY WRITING

Expository writing may be the most "natural" form of expression for middle grade students. As one teacher put it, "Middle school students are tellers—always ready with a bit of information or an idea." In expository writing, students have the opportunity to write in order to share information. How can middle grade students share information? Some of the ways include short reports, research reports, newsletters, brochures, newspaper articles, biographies, autobiographies, a Web page on the Internet, friendly letters and short notes, journals in the content areas (science, social studies), text for radio or television (school shows) projects, and sample expository tasks across the curriculum.

Writing across the curriculum has been a popular method of making communication valid and valuable in all subject areas. Many teachers have taken graduate courses and inservice training that help them use this technique effectively. Below are some simple ideas you can use to try a fresh approach of using expository writing in different disciplines. You can use these ideas as activities or as assessments.

Social Studies Tasks

◆ Use e-mail to write to a pen pal in another country. Use the proper "friendly-letter" format.

◆ Do an Internet search to find information about a current event and then write a short report using that information.

◆ Use CD-ROM technology to do a search on a landform or climatic event in the area of geography. Write a one-minute "radio flash", giving your audience an important update about this. Examples: a shift in the ocean plate, the eruption of a once-dormant volcano, or the "El Niño" weather phenomenon

◆ Use the newspaper (print and on-line) and at least two magazine sources to write a mini-biography of a famous man or woman who is changing the world political scene.

Science or Mathematics Tasks

◆ Keep a journal for science describing your observations. Underline key vocabulary words as you use them in complete sentences to describe what you see, feel, hear, and touch.

◆ After you complete a set of problems in mathematics, write a short note to a friend who may be experiencing trouble with the problem. List the steps you took to solve the problem.

◆ Work with a group to write a five-minute script for a video presentation on a controversial topic, such as cloning, acid rain, or becoming a vegetarian. Use at least two scientific studies to support your report.

◆ Create a Web page in which you detail your class's application of mathematics to the real world. Call this page Middle School Math for Real People.

Emphasis on doing research is included in this section because middle school language arts is the area of the curriculum in which more formal research is introduced. Before you have students do a research project, give them copies of page 23 to complete. Then have students evaluate page 23 using page 24 to see if they are good researchers. Give students pages 25–27 to complete after you assign an expository writing task. Use page 28 to evaluate students' writing.

RESEARCH SKILLS ASSESSMENT

Circle T (true) or F (false) for each item. Then compare your answers to the key (page 24). This is a "Researcher Rating Rubric" just for fun!

1. To do a good job researching a project, start by looking for sources first.   T   F

2. The Internet is the best source for research. Everything you could want to know is on the Web.   T   F

3. It is easier to write down quotes on index cards and then go back and do the bibliography or "Work Cited" page.   T   F

4. An outline is necessary for beginning writers, but if you have done a research report already, it is a poor use of time.   T   F

5. The best researchers work alone.   T   F

6. The school library is the only library that you need to use.   T   F

7. It is acceptable to use someone's idea in a report as long as you list his or her book or article in the bibliography.   T   F

8. In a research report, your opinion is just as important as the experts' opinions.   T   F

9. Print resources, such as encyclopedias, are the most accurate sources of information.   T   F

10. You cannot use interviews in a research paper.   T   F

11. The deductive format is the best way to present a report.   T   F

12. Spelling and grammar aren't as important in research writing as in narrative writing. After all, it is about facts, not about a story.   T   F

KEY FOR THE RESEARCH SKILLS ASSESSMENT

1. False. If you jump right in, you might drown in the facts. It is a good idea to think about what you want to find and do the *Pre-Research Task Analysis* on page 25 first.

2. False. The Internet is an excellent source, but it is not the best or only source that you need. A good researcher uses a variety of sources, comparing them for content and accuracy. The Internet has a lot of good information but a lot of junk, too. Be sure that your Internet source is valid, such as the Web page of a Federal Agency or a University's Science Department, not someone's homepage.

3. False. Don't fall into that trap. As you consult a source, go ahead and prepare a "Citation Card" on it. You can color code all of your Citation Cards (all blue or all green) and keep them together, or an even better trick is to put a colored star on your Citation Card and then stack your note cards from that source behind it, and put a rubber band around the stack.

4. False. An outline is critical. It keeps you focused and organized. A deadline is a good idea, too.

5. False. If your work style or personality makes you more comfortable working alone, then go for it. Try to stretch a bit and at least talk over a few ideas with a partner. Many researchers do collaborate, however, sharing resources and ideas, and this can make the work easier and more robust.

6. False. Branch out and be curious. Did you know that many college libraries welcome younger students? Your public library is a great place to work and probably has a research librarian and Internet access at your disposal.

7. False. You must always quote your source and give credit.

8. False. Opinion weakens a report. A good expository writer adds his or her style or "slant" to the work but doesn't dilute it with opinion.

9. False. Print resources are good, but make sure that they are current (within 3 years).

10. False. Interviews are acceptable as long as you A) clear it with your teacher, B) obtain permission from the interviewee to print his or her ideas, C) use a pre-approved set of interview questions, and D) balance interviews with other forms of information. Interviews are called anecdotal or ethnographic data, and they are very valuable when done correctly.

11. False. Both inductive and deductive formats can be used successfully. The trick is to pick one and stick with it.

12. False. Spelling, grammar, neatness, and accuracy are critical in expository writing. Sloppy work makes all of your research suspect.

Rate your research skills with this rubric!

10 or More Items Correct: You are a resourceful, respectable researcher. You have a balanced and organized plan for getting your facts together and presenting them in an interesting, logical format. You probably enjoy finding out new information and may be an avid reader. You probably enjoy using technology as a tool rather than a toy. You are ready for just about any kind of research-based writing task.

6–10 Items Correct: You are a reasonably ready researcher. You have the right idea about research—find facts and put them together in a logical manner. However, you may need to polish your organizational skills or take some risks trying out new kinds of sources. Have you explored the use of technology to improve your skills? You are ready to research, but you may want to start with a simple project first.

5 or Fewer Items Correct: You are not ready to do research independently. Spend some time learning to write an outline. Visit a library and poke around the research tools, or ask your teacher to arrange a class with a librarian. Research is fun, but you may be missing out.

Name _____ Date _____

PRE-RESEARCH TASK ANALYSIS

Your teacher has assigned an expository writing task. It may be a report, a paper, or something more creative, such as a biography, a case study, or a script for a video. Whatever it is, you need to use research and writing skills to make it happen. This task analysis can help you evaluate your plan for completing the task successfully.

Step One: Write the "due date" of the project. _____

Step Two: List 3–5 dates for working in the library, on the Internet, or with alternative resources to secure your facts.

Date _____ Place _____

Date _____ Place _____

Date _____ Place _____

Date _____ Place _____

Date _____ Place _____

Step Three: Will you work alone or with a team? Explain your decision and list team members if you will be collaborating with other writers.

_____

_____

Step Four: Circle the sources that you plan to investigate as you find facts.

magazines   research journals   CD-ROM technology   books   Internet
interview   newspapers   newsletters   original documents   journals or diaries
biographies   autobiographies   court papers or tax records   videotapes or audiotapes

Step Five: Write a set of questions that describe what you want to know.

Question One _____

Question Two _____

Question Three _____

Question Four _____

• •

Step Six: Identify important facts that you will need to present in your task.

Who? _____

What? _____

When? _____

Where? _____

How? _____

Why? _____

• •

Step Seven: Write whether you will use an inductive or a deductive approach in your presentation and tell why.

_____

_____.

• •

Step Eight: Give your presentation a working title. _____

• •

Step Nine: Gather tools for your job (index cards, pens, pencils, notebook, tape recorder for interviews, etc.).

• •

Step Ten: Determine who your audience will be. Do they already know anything about your topic? Will you be giving a lot of background information? Will you need pictures or drawings?

• •

Step Eleven: Decide how long your project will be before you begin gathering data. _____ pages long

• •

Step Twelve: Ask yourself, "How can I use my personal interests or curiosity to make this project more exciting?" We learn best when our background, experiences, or interests can be used. How can this research help you?

_____

_____

_____

_____

STUDENT PRE-CHECK FOR EXPOSITORY WRITING TASK

Go Back and Look	Yes/No	Source
Did you review your research notes to check the facts, dates, and spelling of names and places?		
Do you know who your audience is and how that will affect your product?		
Did you do an outline of how the facts and ideas will be presented? Will you start from a narrow set of facts and build to a main idea (inductive), or go from a main idea to supporting it with facts (deductive)?		
Did you use paragraphs to move from one idea to another in a logical way?		
Did you use complete sentences and end each sentence with an appropriate mark of punctuation?		
Did you think about the facts and put them together in your own words, or did you string them together directly from the sources?		
If you quoted one of your sources, did you give credit by using quotation marks and showing the page number and author of the quote?		

A 3-POINT RUBRIC FOR EXPOSITORY WRITING

Student_____ Date _____

Evaluator_____ Type of Task _____

3 Points: An Exemplary Expository Piece—The work is easy to read, with a logical development from either the deductive or inductive perspective. Facts and information are woven into the narrative in a way that makes sense. Clearly, the author used his or her own words and didn't "copy from the sources". Spelling and grammar are correct, with no simple errors. A variety of sources are cited, and this makes the product robust and well developed.

2 Points: An Acceptable Expository Piece—The work makes sense, but there may be some flaws in logical development. The writer needs to decide on either an inductive or a deductive perspective and stick with it. Facts and information are used, but they may need to be translated more clearly into the author's "own words". Spelling and grammar are at an acceptable level, with three or fewer simple errors. The author should get a friend to proof the work or use the checklist. An acceptable number of sources are cited.

1 Point: Extra Work Is Needed in Expository Writing—The work doesn't make sense to the reader. What is the author trying to tell the reader about the topic? A list of the facts needs to be made and put in a logical order. The writer's own experiences and opinions are used instead of presenting information from sources. Whole paragraphs may have been pulled from the sources and was not truly the author's own work. Spelling and grammar require attention, with more than three errors that may be simple or complex. This work needs revision.

Points Earned:_____

Comments: _____

_____

_____

_____

_____

_____

TECHNICAL WRITING

Technical writing—is it for engineers or for secretaries? Is it for nurses or for business owners? Is it for middle school students? The answer to all three questions, technically speaking, is yes. Technical writing, for the purpose of this section, is the use of simple, direct language to conduct business or to get a job done. This can include the use of resumes, business forms, letters, directions, or developing manuals. Middle school students should be introduced to this kind of writing and most importantly, the role it plays in our world.

With the advent of "Service Learning" and "Tech Prep" curricula in schools today, students in the middle grades have the chance to explore the world of work from an early age. They may have opportunities to visit offices and factories and to meet men and women who have established themselves in technical careers. However, most youngsters fail to realize that all of the technical career fields have one thing in common—a reliance on communication skills. In fact, many young people may think that if they choose a more technical career, they can avoid English or writing. This, of course, is not the case.

With the advent of technology and the spread of flexible work choices, many workers in the new millennium will work alone in the field, almost like an independent contractor. Or, if they are in a plant or office, they will have less middle management supervision. Strong technical writing skills will be sought after by employers and will be even more critical to the success of workers. To get your students motivated, ask them to respond to the oral quiz below about technical writing.

Are you ready for the techno-lit world?

1. Would you know how to write a business letter asking your employer to add dental insurance to your health plan?

2. If you were asked to review a policy or a new product for your boss, could you write a memo that you could be proud of?

3. How would you approach the task of writing a "Self-Evaluation" that might lead to a raise or promotion for you?

4. Could you write directions for using a piece of software and e-mail it to a co-worker who was 100 miles away?

5. If your dream job came open today, how persuasive would your resume sound?

6. If you left your child with a new baby sitter, could you write a clear, easy-to-follow schedule about his or her medicine, feeding, and sleeping schedules?

7. If you worked in the medical field, could you write notes on charts that made sense and that might impact someone in a life or death situation?

Use pages 30 and 31 to evaluate students' pieces of technical writing. After evaluation, go over the pages carefully with students to show where they can improve.

CHECKLIST FOR TECHNICAL WRITING
7-POINT SCALE

Student _____   Type of Technical Writing_____

Instructor _____   Period _____ Date_____

For each criteria, circle 1 if the piece of writing meets the criteria. Circle 0 is the piece does not meet it.

Criteria	Points Earned	Comments
Does the product follow the correct format?	0 1	
Does the product use technical words or phrases appropriately?	0 1	
Is the product free of spelling or grammatical errors?	0 1	
Is the product free of jargon and extraneous language?	0 1	
Does the product use bullets, lists, or graphs where necessary?	0 1	
Is the product written in a logical sequence?	0 1	
Does the product do the job it was designed to do?	0 1	

A POSTCARD ASSESSMENT FOR A BUSINESS LETTER

Dear _____ ,
(student)

I'm sorry, but we were not able to fill your order or request because:

1. We could not read your writing, or spelling errors made your request hard to understand. _____

2. You did not write in a logical sequence. We could not follow your train of thought. _____

3. Your writing style was not professional. It contained extra information, opinion, or was rude. _____

4. You did not state your request or your order clearly, giving all the necessary information. _____

5. You did not include important details, such as your daytime phone number, address, or part number that you need. _____

6. You did not follow the correct format for a business letter. _____

7. You did not supply enough background information to make your case. _____

Sincerely,

_____

PERSUASIVE WRITING

Are middle grade students influenced by persuasive writing and other forms of media? Definitely. In fact, one might make the case that young adolescents are the most easily persuaded age group. Here's why:

1. Hormone surges might make youngsters emotional and volatile. They can be carried away by emotion.

2. Peer pressure or opinions can make young teens buckle and bend. They want to conform and thus can be persuaded easily to move to the side where their friends are clustered.

3. Youngsters in middle grades are looking for a side to join. They may not be clinging to their parents' views as much, but they haven't lived long enough to form their own, so they are open to persuasive arguments.

Middle school students need to learn to recognize and analyze persuasive writing as much as, if not more than, they need to learn to design persuasive pieces. To help them get started, give each student a copy of page 33, *Advertisement Analysis*. Have students find an advertisement to analyze using this page as a guide. This is a relevant way to introduce persuasive writing to youngsters. Then give students a copy of page 34 to get them on-task with the art of persuasive writing. You can give them this page before they start a piece of writing or after they finish a piece of persuasive writing. Use page 35 to evaluate students' pieces of writing.

Name _____ Date _____

ADVERTISEMENT ANALYSIS—HOW DISCERNING ARE YOU?

• •

Advertisement Analyzed _____

Source _____ Date of Publication _____

• •

Find an advertisement. Use it to answer the questions below.

1. What is the real message of this advertisement? _____
   _____

2. What kinds of appeals are used to get your attention? Circle all that apply. Then describe one in detail.

   kids your age   beauty and health   bandwagon   culture or ethnicity
   romance   nature   money/status   violence or breaking limits
   brainy   celebrity appeal   "tug at the heartstrings"   statistics or startling facts

   Description of Chosen Ad _____
   _____

3. How does this advertisement fit or clash with your values? _____
   _____

4. How do the use of pictures, color, and design make this advertisement persuasive?
   _____

5. Are there any symbols used that may evoke feelings or ideas that are not overtly stated?
   _____

6. Can you name any words that have double or hidden meanings or a connotation that is persuasive?
   _____

7. Did you change your mind about the product after studying the advertisement? Why or why not?
   _____

8. Does the name of the product help "sell it"? Can you identify the reasons why this name was selected or developed?
   _____

9. Can you figure out why the design or packaging of the product works to persuade you?
   _____

10. Is this product aimed at adults or teens? How do you know this?
    _____

DID YOU CONVINCE YOUR READER?
A CHECKLIST FOR PERSUASIVE WRITING

Circle the task: Advertisement   Editorial   Essay   Fund-Raising Letter   Persuasive Letter   Political Poster

◆◆ **Rating Key:** P = powerful   M = moderate   W = weak level of persuasion

Criteria	Rating		
1. Did you spend time analyzing your audience?	P	M	W
2. Did you spend time choosing words that have the right "connotation" or twist?	P	M	W
3. Is your "appeal" the right one for this task? (i.e., bandwagon, beauty, brains)	P	M	W
4. Did you attack on several levels, giving a number of reasons to choose your side or product?	P	M	W
5. Did you attempt to weaken the "other side"?	P	M	W
6. Is your design attractive and easy-to-follow?	P	M	W
7. Do grammar and spelling make your product strong and professional?	P	M	W
8. Do you express a genuine, believable tone?	P	M	W

RUBRIC FOR PERSUASIVE WRITING
3-POINT SCALE

Student _____ Date _____

Powerfully Persuasive—3 Points "You're ready for politics or Madison Avenue!"

- ◆ The writer uses language masterfully to make his or her point.
- ◆ The writer's use of grammar and spelling is appropriate and correct.
- ◆ The writer clearly knows the audience.
- ◆ The writer selects an "appeal" and uses it well. (More than one appeal may be used to strengthen the message.)
- ◆ Both facts and opinion are used to form the argument.

Moderately Persuasive—2 Points "You are making a point!"

- ◆ The writer uses language that makes his or her point but may not be very persuasive.
- ◆ The writer's use of grammar and spelling are acceptable, but there may be a few minor errors.
- ◆ The writer knows the audience.
- ◆ The writer selects an appeal but may not tap into all of the power available in that appeal.
- ◆ The writer may be relying too heavily on either fact or opinion.

Weak Form of Persuasion—1 or 0 Points (Revision Needed)

- ◆ This work does not make use of persuasive language.
- ◆ Spelling and grammar usage are poor and dilute the power of the work.
- ◆ The writer is unclear about the audience and the appeal that would be most effective.
- ◆ There are few facts to back up the argument, and opinion, if used, is not reasonable.

Points Earned: _____

Comments: _____

_____

_____

_____

Name _____ Date _____

PROOFREADING CHECKLIST FOR LANGUAGE ARTS

ELEMENTS	YES	NO	CHECK ITEM
Spelling			
used a spell check program			
used consistent spelling			
checked foreign words			
checked spelling of names and places			
Capital Letters			
beginning of each sentence			
proper nouns			
initials (U.N. for United Nations)			
months of the year			
Period			
at end of sentences			
after abbreviations (Mr.)			
after initials (J. Smith)			
Comma			
words in a series			
between city and state			
between day and year			
after a greeting in a friendly letter			
before the conjunction in a compound sentence			
after a dependent clause at the beginning of a sentence			
after a noun of direct address			

. . . .

ELEMENTS	YES	NO	CHECK ITEM
Question Mark			
at the end of a questioning sentence			
Exclamation Point			
at the end of a sentence or a word that shows excitement			
Apostrophe			
in contractions			
to show possession (Joe's dog)			
Quotation Marks			
around direct quotations			
around a title of a poem, story, song, or television program			
Book Title			
underlined (Where the Flowers Grow)			
Colon			
before a list of items			
in writing time of day			
business letter greeting			
Hyphen			
compound words (sometimes)			
compound numbers			
to divide a word at the end of a line of text			

Name _____ Date _____

ELEMENTS	YES	NO	CHECK ITEM
Agreement			
subject and verb			
singular and plural			
Voice (Active or Passive)			
consistent within the paper			
avoids the passive voice			
uses active voice if the subject acts			
Structure and Content			
shorter sentences			
correct use of paragraphs			
order and logic in sentences			
superfluous articles and prepositions			
no jargon, unless it is in dialogue			
appropriate words or phrases			
Common Spelling Errors			
Weather/Whether			
There/Their/They're			
Affect or *Effect*			
Your or *You're*			
Its or *It's*			

Chapter Two
Assessment in Mathematics

Introduction

Something to Think About:
"A correct answer is like an affectionate kiss."
(Goethe)

Middle school students are at a real crossroads in their abilities to process mathematics. Developmentally, eleven- and twelve-year-olds are moving into a period in which they ought to be able to deal with abstract concepts. As most middle school math teachers know, this is not always the case.

Below are some facts about mathematics and middle school students followed by ideas you might find helpful when dealing with these situations.

- ◆ Mathematics is a discipline that relies heavily on prior knowledge and experience. Abstract concepts cannot be introduced effectively unless the proper sequence of skills has been mastered by the student.

  Assessment Message: Do a pre-test or skill check before introducing a concept.

- ◆ Middle school youngsters are often concerned more with the "here and now" than with the distant future.

  Assessment Message: Construct assessments and tasks that use real-life situations to demonstrate how mathematics can be truly meaningful and useful for students.

- ◆ Middle school youngsters are very social, but they also need to develop skills in independent thinking and in scheduling their time. They also need to develop values, such as perseverance.

  Assessment Message: Balance cooperative projects with independent assessment tasks. Students need to learn how to do both.

- ◆ Mathematics can be a challenge for middle school girls because of both social and hormonal influences. New research suggests that estrogen surges may make it hard for girls to concentrate.

  Assessment Message: Give middle school girls attention and support, especially in upper level math courses. Don't let them take the easy way out.

Materials in Chapter Two and How to Use Them

In this chapter, you will find activities for students to complete in order to review math material, refresh their minds, or practice skills prior to the formal assessment. *The Algebra Glossary* (pages 47–50) is a great way to help students move from concrete to abstract in their thinking about mathematics. Having students use the correct terms is imperative if we want them to be able to ask questions about and process the more sophisticated math found in middle school. Below and on page 40 are 10 creative ways for you to use this glossary.

1. If students have algebra portfolios, make copies of the glossaries and have students staple them to their inside front covers. Students can work independently to fill in their glossaries.

2. Do a "term of the week". Let students add to their glossary checklists as you progress through the year.

3. Create an "Algebra Glossary" bulletin board displaying examples of students' work that exemplify use of specific terms. Students can use their own glossaries as checkpoints and reviewing tools.

4. Students can "quiz" one another on terms and record their answers on their checklists.

5. Students can do an "open book" chapter test for extra points and record findings on their checklists.

6. Students can use their checklists with a tutor to help them "catch up".

7. Do a "Daily Algebra" riddle with the answer being found in the glossary.

8. Use the glossary as a homework helper. Students can put the glossaries in their notebooks to refer to when they have questions.

9. Send the glossaries home as a form of parent communication and as a study tool for tests.

10. Assist visual learners by writing answers in bold red or orange marker or pen.

The pages listed below are for students to use prior to formal assessment.

◆ *Applied Mathematics Assessment Task* (page 41) can be used for any kind of math problem project. It is generic, yet it takes the students through steps for solving a problem.

◆ *The Algebra Glossary* (pages 47–50)

◆ *Are You a Problem Solver?* (page 52) Give this activity to students to help them get in the correct mode of thinking about mathematics.

◆ *How Am I Doing?* (page 55) This form is for students to use to help them keep up with assignments and averages.

The pages below are for teachers to use as evaluation tools. These pages give you options for doing assessments in some traditional or authentic ways. Students can be heavily involved in the "tasks," or assessment can be more teacher-directed. Two kinds of rubrics are offered on pages 53 and 54 to meet the pacing and expectations of your instruction.

◆ *Applied Mathematics Checklist* (page 42)

◆ *Pre-Algebra Checklist* (page 43)

◆ *Measurement Skills Checklist* (page 44)

◆ *Geometry Checklist* (page 45)

◆ *Algebra Checklist* (page 46)

◆ *Create Your Own Mathematics Terms Glossary* (page 51) Use this open-ended form to design glossaries for specific units of study or for groups of students who require individualized instruction or enrichment.

◆ *5-Point Math Rubric* (page 53)

◆ *3-Point Rubric for Math Tasks* (page 54)

Name _____ Date _____

APPLIED MATHEMATICS ASSESSMENT TASK

Course _____ Period _____

Write your task below. Complete the task in the work area. Then respond to the questions at the bottom of the page.

Your task is _____

─────────────── **Work Area** ───────────────

List the steps that you followed to solve this task. Use the numbered boxes to show your work in the correct order.

1	2	3

The correct answer is _____.

APPLIED MATHEMATICS CHECKLIST

Student _____ Date of Evaluation _____

Evaluator _____ Period/Class _____

CRITERIA	RATING SCALE		
	With Difficulty	Proficiently	Expertly
Addition Skills			
Subtraction Skills			
Multiplication Skills			
Division Skills			
Consumer Math Skills (money, banking)			
Word Problems			
Solves Problems Using Decimals			
Solves Problems Using Fractions (simple and mixed)			
Recognizes and Uses Roman Numerals			
Solves Problems Involving Calculation of Time and Distance			
Uses Graphs and Tables to Supply Answers to Questions			
Graphs Simple Data in a Neat and Usable Format			
Measurement (standard)			
Measurement (metric)			

PRE-ALGEBRA CHECKLIST

Student _____ Date of Evaluation _____

Evaluator _____ Period/Class _____

SKILL	MASTERY LEVEL		
	Experiencing Difficulty	Working Toward Mastery	Complete Mastery
Understands the concepts of variables as a place value for unknown integers			
Understands the concept of variable expressions and equations			
Is able to order and compare integers using the number line			
Successfully graphs ordered pairs in a coordinate plane			
Uses problem-solving tools to solve pre-algebraic equations			
Solves real-world problems using algebraic concepts such as variables and open sentences			
Explains the steps used to solve a pre-algebra problem			

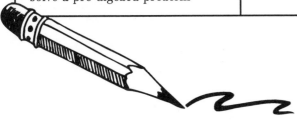

MEASUREMENT SKILLS CHECKLIST

Student _____ Date of Evaluation _____

Evaluator _____ Period/Class_____

Measurement Skill	Mastery Yes/No	Tools Used in Mastery
Converts from standard to metric system		
Estimates length, weight, and capacity in standard units		
Estimates length, weight, and capacity in metric units		
Solves for length, weight, and capacity in standard units		
Solves for length, weight, and capacity in metric units		
Reads maps to scale using standard and metric units (miles, meters)		
Determines elapsed time		
Determines temperature in Celsius and Fahrenheit		
Uses measurement to solve real-life tasks		

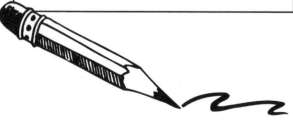

GEOMETRY CHECKLIST

Student _____   Grade Level _____

Teacher _____

Skill	Date of Mastery	Problems Experienced
Identifies and classifies two- and three-dimensional geometric figures		
Demonstrates spatial sense by constructing or drawing two- and three-dimensional shapes		
Solves for perimeter and area of polygons		
Solves for the circumference and area of circles		
Solves for volume and surface area of figures		
Identifies and uses the following terms with accuracy: *point, line, plane, line segment, parallel lines, vertex, perpendicular lines, ray, diameter, radius, arc, circumference, area, polygon, intersecting lines, space, regular polygon*		
Demonstrates ability to use the concept of congruency in problem solving		
Demonstrates the ability to use the concepts of parallelism, perpendicularity, and symmetry to solve problems		
Uses the Pythagorean Theorem to find the missing side of a right triangle		
Graphs points on a coordinate plane		

ALGEBRA CHECKLIST

Student _____   Date _____

Evaluator _____   Grade Level _____

Course _____

Algebra is a process of understanding and application. Use this checklist to document students' growth over time and their degree of competency.

Algebraic Concept	With Ease 3	With Practice 2	With Difficulty 1
Identifies and uses the critical terms listed on *The Algebra Glossary* (pages 47–50)			
Performs operations on integers and rational numbers			
Uses techniques for estimation			
Applies concepts of variables, expressions, equations, and inequalities			
Represents situations that involve variable quantities by using expressions, equations, and matrices			
Uses formulas to design and solve real-life problems using algebra			
Uses algebraic skills to solve problems involving operations and inequalities			
Applies knowledge of probability and statistics to estimate and solve problems			

Name _____ Date _____

THE ALGEBRA GLOSSARY

Evaluate your knowledge of the terms below that are integral to understanding the concepts of algebra.

My Level of Understanding				
Term	**High** *	**Average** +	**Low** N	**Write an example here.**
Adding 0 Property				
algebraic factorization				
Associative Property				
average of a group of numbers				
axes				
base of an exponent				
Commutative Property				
composite number				
coordinates				
cosine of an angle				
data				
decimal				
dependent events				
digits				
Distributive Property				

GA-1671 Middle Grade Assessments

Name _____   Date _____

My Level of Understanding				
Term	**High** *	**Average** +	**Low** N	**Write an example here.**
equation				
estimate				
evaluate an expression				
even number				
expectation				
exponent				
expression				
factors				
formula				
frequency table				
independent events				
inequality				
integers				
inverse operations				
least common multiple				
like terms				
linear equality				

GA-1671 Middle Grade Assessments

Name _____   Date _____

My Level of Understanding				
Term	**High** *	**Average** +	**Low** N	**Write an example here.**
linear equation				
mean, median, mode				
multiple				
Multiplying by 1 Property				
negative number				
odds				
operation				
opposites				
ordered pair				
origin				
outcome				
percent				
permutation				
pi				
positive number				
power				
prime factorization				

My Level of Understanding				
Term	**High** *	**Average** +	**Low** N	**Write an example here.**
prime number				
probability				
Pythagorean Theorem				
range				
ratio				
rational number				
reciprocal				
repeating decimal				
sample space				
scientific notation				
square root				
statistics				
Symmetric Property of Equality				
system of equations				
variable				
vertex				
whole number				

CREATE YOUR OWN MATHEMATICS TERMS GLOSSARY

Name _____

Course _____ Teacher _____

| Term | My Level of Understanding | | | Write an example here. |
	High *	Average +	Low N	

ARE YOU A PROBLEM SOLVER?
CHECK YOUR MATHEMATICS MASTERY

1. I always check my work before accepting the answer as correct.   Yes   No

2. I use technology to make my work faster and more accurate.   Yes   No

3. I know how to write down steps in solving a problem.   Yes   No

4. I feel comfortable looking at examples from the textbook and then applying them to a new situation.   Yes   No

5. I use what I already know about math to ease into a new situation or challenge.   Yes   No

6. I give myself adequate time to work on mathematics homework.   Yes   No

7. I look for a pattern or logical sequence in a math problem.   Yes   No

8. I practice with several simple examples before going on to a more complex problem.   Yes   No

5-POINT MATH RUBRIC

Student_____ Date _____

Evaluator_____ Type of Task _____

Review the student's or group's answer or performance and use this rubric to award points. If the criteria was met, circle 1. If it was not met, circle 0. Total the points.

◆◆ **Key:** 4–5 points—acceptable   3–4 points—review   0–3 points—reteach

1. The answer is correct, and the response shows   0   1
   accuracy in calculation/development.

2. The appropriate operation or formula was used   0   1
   to develop the response.

3. The answer makes sense and is written with the   0   1
   correct terms and/or abbreviations.

4. The work area shows that the student(s) used data,   0   1
   charts, drawing, and "figuring" to solve the problem.

5. It is clear from the student's(s') response that   0   1
   the mathematical concept or construct is clearly
   understood and applied.

   Total Points Awarded _____

3-POINT RUBRIC FOR MATH TASKS

Student_____   Date _____

Evaluator_____   Type of Task _____

3 POINTS—MATH MANIAC

◆ You solved for the correct answer.

◆ You listed the steps in a logical order.

◆ You used all terms appropriately and explained your solution.

◆ You were able to apply previously learned math skills.

◆ You used tools such as a calculator, protractor, and meter stick appropriately.

2 POINTS—MATH MOVER

◆ You are moving toward the correct answer, but a simple error kept you from the "maniac" level.

◆ You listed the correct steps, but your order may not be logical.

◆ You can use the terms but may need more practice applying them to new situations.

◆ You have an understanding of the skills previously learned.

◆ You used tools such as a calculator, protractor, and meter stick appropriately.

1–0 POINTS—MATH MISER

◆ You did not solve for the correct answer, and your work showed that your errors are multiple.

◆ You were not able to show a logical sequence of steps needed to solve this problem.

◆ You need to review terminology needed to solve this task.

◆ You may need to review an earlier skill.

◆ Your inability to use tools appropriately interfered with this task.

Points Earned: _____

Comments:_____

_____

_____

Recommendation: Move on in math.   Do a few more examples.   *(circle one)*

Remediation Needed: _____

_____

_____

How Am I Doing?

Student_____   Grading Period_____

Teacher _____   Class _____

Test Name and Grade	**Group Project Grades or Points Earned**
_____	_____
_____	_____
_____	
_____	**Individual Projects Points or Grades**
_____	_____
	_____
Homework Grades	**Math Notebook or Journal**
_____	_____
_____	
_____	**Points or Grade for Class Participation**
_____	_____

Add all grades or points earned and solve for the average. How are you doing? Where are your weak points? How can you improve? Where can you find help?

_____

_____

My average is _____. Signature _____

CHAPTER THREE
ASSESSMENT IN GEOGRAPHY AND SOCIAL STUDIES

INTRODUCTION

Something to Think About:
"Heaven on earth."
(John Milton)

Middle grade students should be quite comfortable with the larger questions of geography. After all, they are always wondering "Where am I?" or "Where am I going next?" The study of geography and social studies is particularly meaningful for young adolescents because they are making giant steps from concrete to abstract thought. The fascinating issues of culture, world peace, trade, traditions, and politics begin to take on more meaning for them.

In middle grade social studies, teachers are responsible for instruction in these six areas:

◆ Geography

◆ History

◆ Economics

◆ Anthropology/Sociology

◆ Political Science

◆ Civics

Charged with this daunting span of curriculum to address, it is no wonder that many savvy teachers use integrated units of instruction to connect the disciplines. Moreover, since geography is such a rich and concrete place to begin instruction, one can use the 1994 *National Geography Standards* as a basis for both curriculum and assessment.

The *Geography Standards* frame out 18 criteria for what the "geographically informed person knows and understands." These standards can be grouped into six curricular strands:

◆ The use of maps, globes, and atlases to study spatial relationships in geography

◆ The study of places and regions

◆ The study of physical systems and patterns of landforms

◆ The study of how people and cultures are influenced by geography and how geography influences culture and people

◆ The study of how natural resources are used by people

◆ The connection of geography to past, present, and future

The *Standards* also offer specific details on what students in grades 5–8 should know. It is these specific criteria that one should apply when designing assessment in middle school social studies. As assessment tools are created, it should involve a look at how students can do the following:

1) ask geographic questions, 2) acquire geographic information, 3) organize geographic information, 4) analyze geographic information, and 5) answer geographic questions.

Geography shapes the rest of middle school social studies because important economic, historical, political, and cultural issues are embedded in first understanding how Earth itself influences the choices and decisions that people and cultures make over time.

Materials in Chapter Three and How to Use Them

In the middle grades, teachers are responsible for presenting curriculum in the areas of geography, history, economics, anthropology/sociology, political science, and civics. That's an enormous undertaking, so many teachers turn to the "project method," or some form of integrated instruction. A theme, novel, film, or current event may be the focal point for a set of lessons in social studies. However, because of its concrete nature and its close ties to science, geography often becomes the main social science that is studied in middle school. Hence, the 1994 *National Geography Standards* were used to frame out the instructional and evaluative tools included in this chapter.

The pages listed below are designed to be completed by the student.

◆ *Sample Geography Task* (page 63)—Use this open-ended instructional activity to cover a spectrum of thinking skills. You (or the students) supply the current event and then geography skills are applied to analyze the event.

◆ *Cultural Update* (page 64)—This is another student-driven activity that prepares students for assessment. Use this as a research project, cooperative task, ongoing project, or enrichment activity. It involves research skills, cultural geography, and public speaking skills. The purposes of *Cultural Update* are to 1) make students more culturally literate, 2) offer the students an opportunity to do research, and 3) practice oral presentation skills.

◆ *Create a Geo-File* (page 65)—This activity is done by students and then evaluated by you using the *4-Point Rubric for the Geo-File Task* on page 66. Make 50 copies of the bottom of the page for each student to use to write his or her clues. After the assessments of the cards has been completed, have students quiz each other using the cards.

◆ The U.S. and world maps on pages 67–68 provide students with resources to solve many geography tasks that you might create.

The pages below can be used by you for evaluation.

◆ *Checklist for Using Maps and Globes* (page 59)—The use of maps and globes and other media is critical to instruction. Don't forget to evaluate these skills which support knowledge of these facts.

◆ *Checklist for Understanding Physical Systems* (page 60)—Physical systems include the climate, landforms, and environment of Earth.

◆ *Checklist for Cultural Geography* (page 61)—Do your students understand how culture impacts trade, transportation, the economy, and human populations? This is a critical social studies area that is seldom evaluated.

◆ *3-Point Rubric for a Social Studies Project* (page 62)—Designed for use with authentic, long-term projects in which students must examine a set of concepts from many perspectives, this rubric can match any content area that you and the students choose.

◆ *4-Point Rubric for the Geo-File Task* (page 66)—Use this rubric to evaluate students' knowledge of geography on the cards they created in the activity *Create a Geo-File* (page 65).

CHECKLIST FOR USING MAPS AND GLOBES

Student_____   Date _____

The student can . . .	His or her skill level is . . .		
select the appropriate tool: a map, globe, atlas, or computer (CD).	High	Average	Poor
identify continents, countries, cities, mountains, rivers, oceans, and other places and landforms by name using a map, globe, or atlas.	High	Average	Poor
use a globe, map, or atlas to interpret information about people and geography.	High	Average	Poor
apply skill in using lines of latitude and longitude, the compass rose, and a map key.	High	Average	Poor
determine distance using maps.	High	Average	Poor
demonstrate skill in using a globe, map, or atlas to predict changes or trends.	High	Average	Poor
compare differences in geography using maps.	High	Average	Poor
describe characteristics of places: climate, population density, elevation.	High	Average	Poor
use different kinds of maps, such as aerial photographs, large scale maps, and contour maps.	High	Average	Poor

CHECKLIST FOR UNDERSTANDING PHYSICAL SYSTEMS

Student_____ Date _____

Key Concept The student understands that . . .	Project or Task (report, project, study, poster, group presentation, story, media)	Rating High (3) Average (2) Poor (1)
erosion produces change in landforms.		
earthquakes and volcanic activity produce change.		
ocean circulation systems affect climates around the world.		
maps and graphs can be used to analyze information about climate and change.		
Earth-sun relationships affect change in physical systems.		
world agricultural patterns and problems can be explained by physical and weather systems.		
the production of power is impacted by physical systems.		
the production of fossil fuels is related to physical systems.		
Earth's ecosystems are interdependent.		
human systems can change physical systems and ecosystems in powerful ways.		

CHECKLIST FOR CULTURAL GEOGRAPHY

Student_____   Date _____

Key Concept The student understands that . . .	Demonstration of Understanding (project, test, story, presentation)	Level of Understanding High (3) Average (2) Poor (1)
population growth affects the way people live.		
population patterns impact the mosaic of a society (age, gender).		
migration patterns shape culture and countries.		
culture plays a role in habitats and landscapes.		
geography and culture shape the economic landscape.		
geography and culture shape transportation and trade.		
rural and urban cultures are shaped by human systems.		
politics and conflicts are shaped by the ways people use resources.		
cultural markers such as holidays, foods, costumes, and religious connections are shaped by geography and diffusion of people from place to place.		

3-POINT RUBRIC FOR A SOCIAL STUDIES PROJECT

Student_____   Group or Individual Project _____

Title of Project _____   Key Concept(s) _____

Date _____   Evaluator _____

◆◆ **Grading Scale:** The project will be awarded 3, 2, or 1 to describe the overall effort, demonstration of knowledge, and level of understanding that the individual or group earned.

3 The project demonstrates a high level of understanding of the key concept(s). There are numerous examples of how physical and human systems are impacted by the concept(s), and they are organized in a meaningful way. The writing is clear, and the use of visual aids is appropriate and contributes to the understanding of the concept(s). It is clear that the student knows how geography, history, anthropology, economics, political science, and/or civics contribute to the development of this key concept(s). The overall impact of the project is powerful and helps others understand the key concept(s).

Comments: _____

2 The project demonstrates an adequate level of understanding of the key concept(s). There is one or more examples of how physical and human systems are impacted by the concept(s), and they are organized in a way that makes sense to the evaluator. The writing is acceptable, though there may be some simple errors in style or substance that detract from the overall impact of the product. Visual aids are neat and clear. The student has an understanding of how geography, history, anthropology, economics, political science, and/or civics contribute to the key concept(s), but there may be some confusion as to the extent or relationship between them. The overall impact of the project is fair, and the student has learned something about the key concept(s).

Comments: _____

1 The project is unacceptable for the geography/social studies student in the middle grades. The key concept(s) is not fully developed, or the project is not complete. Writing and visual aids are not developed at an acceptable level (sloppy or incomplete). The overall impact of the project is weak, and the student needs to revisit the areas of geography, history, anthropology, economics, political science, and/or civics and do more research and thinking. Revise and resubmit.

Comments: _____

Name _____   Date _____

SAMPLE GEOGRAPHY TASK

❖❖ **Materials Needed:** copies of the daily newspaper (national or city), one copy of the world map per student (page 67), colored pens, four index cards per student

Select an article about an important world event (i.e., a famine, a war, a big trade agreement). Working in a cooperative group of four, address the following question: "How does geography (physical and human systems) impact this change or situation?" Your team should investigate each issue together, but each team member is responsible for completing the data, fact, and/or summary on the index cards.

 Card One—red pen and index card: Use the world map to describe the location and geographic systems that contribute to this change or situation.

 Card Two—blue pen and index card: Describe how culture and/or human systems play a role in the change or situation.

 Card Three—green pen and index card: Describe how ecosystems and/or the environment may be changed by the situation.

 Card Four—black pen and index card: Evaluate how this change or situation may fit into what has happened in the past and what may occur in the future, based on geography/social studies.

Name _____ Date _____

CULTURAL UPDATE . . . A WEEKLY TASK FOR MIDDLE SCHOOL STUDENTS

• •

Working in pairs, take a culture each week and write a brief Cultural Update below to present to the class.

• •

_____ Cultural Update on _____
(Students' names)   (culture)

This is your friendly _____ Middle School reporter with 10 facts that you need to

know about the _____ culture. This group of people lives in and around the area

of _____ on the continent of _____.

Geography plays an important role in this culture because _____

_____. You probably know that this group of people speaks

_____, but did you know that they are best known for

making or doing _____? The people from this cultural group celebrate

_____ as an important holiday, and their religious ties are to

_____. Today, this population is growing/not growing because of these factors:

_____

_____

_____

_____.

One interesting new fact that we learned about this culture is _____

_____.

If you compare this culture to ours, you might find that _____

_____

_____

_____

_____.

Name _____ Date _____

CREATE A GEO-FILE . . . TO FILE AWAY GEOGRAPHY KNOWLEDGE

In this activity, you are going to create 50 "Geo Cards"— 10 for each of the following five categories: 1) Important Landforms, 2) Culture Counts, 3) Trade and Economics, 4) City vs. Country, and 5) The Environment and Geography. Use the U.S. and world maps on pages 67–68, as well as other resources, to create the cards.

On each card, write several clues involving a topic for each of the categories. For example: "Use the U.S. map to find my name. I am an Atlantic coast state with a rich history of pirates and Native American legends. The treacherous coastline borders Virginia to the north and my southern cousin that shares a name on the south. What state am I?"

Category_____Card #_____

Geo Card Form

Question: _____

_____

_____

_____

_____

Answer: _____

4-POINT RUBRIC FOR THE GEO-FILE TASK

Student_____ Date _____

4 Points

- ◆ The map(s) or other resources are used correctly.
- ◆ The content is accurate.
- ◆ The questions are interesting and make sense.
- ◆ The right number of cards are included in each of the five categories.
- ◆ The task cards are neatly prepared.
- ◆ An answer (correct) is provided.

3 Points

- ◆ The map(s) or other resources are used but may have a few errors in content and/or accuracy.
- ◆ There are a few too many cards in one category or another.
- ◆ Most of the questions are interesting and make sense, but a few need some work.
- ◆ The task cards are neatly prepared, but there may be a few simple errors.
- ◆ A few answers are missing, or they are incorrect.

2 Points

- ◆ The questions are too simple and do not show understanding of geography and social studies.
- ◆ There are too many questions in one category and not enough in another.
- ◆ Some cards do not have answers.
- ◆ There are multiple spelling or content errors on the cards.

0–1 Points

- ◆ The project is incomplete or too sloppy to evaluate. Revise and resubmit.

Your overall score is_____. Comments: _____

_____

_____

OUTLINE OF WORLD MAP

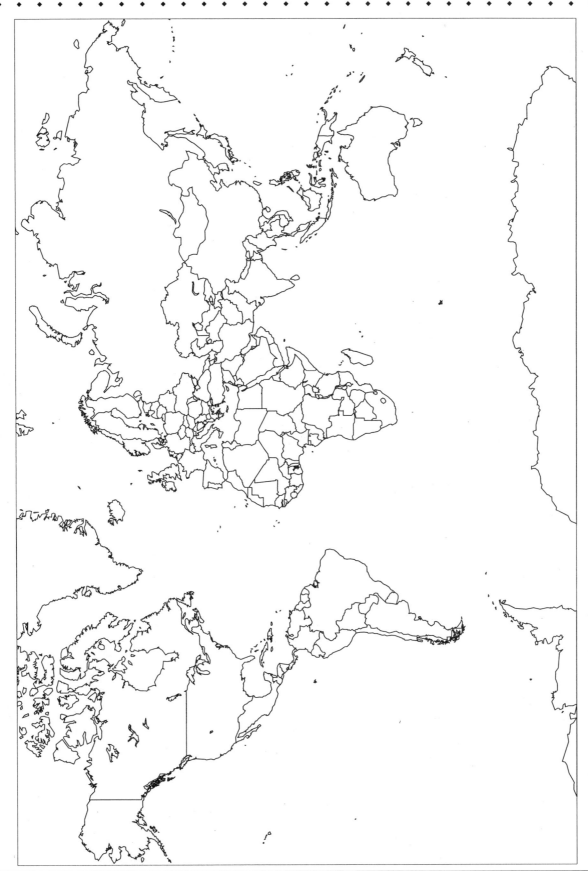

OUTLINE OF U.S. MAP

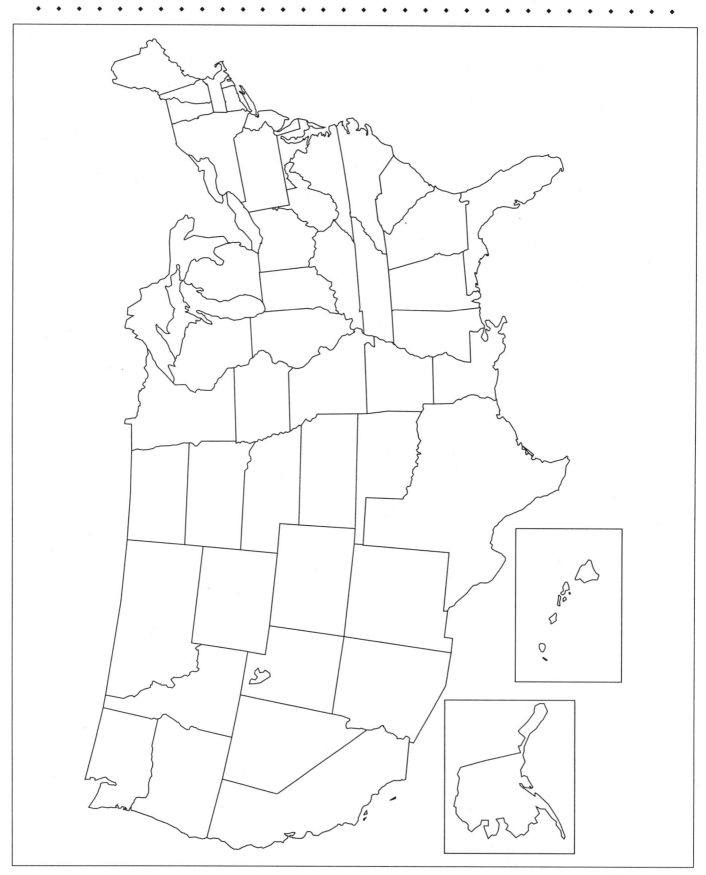

CHAPTER FOUR
ASSESSMENT IN SCIENCE

INTRODUCTION

Something to Think About:
"As soon as a man does not take his existence for granted, but beholds it as something unfathomably mysterious, thought begins."
(Albert Schweitzer)

Can we "teach" middle grade students to be more intelligent? According to Dr. David Perkins, in his provocative book, *Outsmarting IQ* (1995), *reflective intelligence* can be taught in the classroom. "Strategies for memory, problem solving, mental management, and positive attitudes toward investing mental effort" (p. 115) should be the focus of our instruction, according to Perkins. Perhaps science instruction and assessment, more than any other area of the curriculum, offer teachers the opportunity to practice the art of teaching intelligence. It is in science, with the emphasis on *process skills*, that teaching youngsters to be smarter seems to be almost inevitable, if the teacher plans and practices the appropriate strategies.

With assessment in mind, teaching for intelligence takes on new meaning. Middle grade teachers can use assessment as a tool for showing students how to exercise their brains through the following:

◆ Observation and Illustration

◆ Classification and Comparison

◆ Analyzing and Collecting Data

◆ Asking Critical Questions and Making Hypotheses

◆ Investigation and Measurement

◆ Communicating Findings

Materials in Chapter Four and How to Use Them

In science education, from kindergarten to college, the science process skills are taught, applied, used, and reinforced throughout the curriculum. Therefore, the *Process Skills Checklist* (page 71) is the first item in the chapter. It is designed for you to use to evaluate students' overall ability to use each of the skills presented over an extended period of time.

Moreover, an examination of scope and sequence charts and science standards from most states will show that life, earth, physical, and environmental sciences become more differentiated at the middle school level. Hence, you see separate checklists for each of these areas. These checklists are very broad and are meant to serve as a supplement to more specific tests that you create. These checklists can be used to report on *growth over time*.

The teacher-directed assessment tools in this chapter are listed below. These pages are designed for you to use to evaluate and report on student progress.

◆ *Process Skills Checklist* (page 71)

◆ *Life Science Checklist* (page 72) Covers the beginnings of botany and zoology at the middle grade level

◆ *Life Science Checklist II* (page 73) Covers the introductory levels of biology, nutrition, and health

◆ *Earth Science Checklist* (page 74) Covers weather and astronomy

◆ *Earth Science Checklist II* (page 75) Covers fossils, geology, and volcanoes

◆ *Physical Science Checklist* (page 76) Covers energy, matter, electricity, and beginning physics

◆ *Environmental Science Checklist* (page 77) Covers natural resources, endangered species, and global change

◆ *3-Point Rubric for a Science Task* (page 78) This is an open-ended rubric that can be applied to any science content area. Use this for group projects or long-term individual projects.

◆ *Science Fair Project Evaluation* (page 79) Ever wondered how to evaluate those hundreds of middle school science fair projects? Here's a simple scale using "beakers" as a visual representation of effort and excellence.

This chapter also features two student-driven activities which are designed to help students practice, review, and apply the science process skills across areas of life, earth, physical, and environmental science. These pages are listed below.

◆ *Science Vocabulary Checkpoint* (page 80) The correct use of vocabulary words is critical, but it takes time and practice. Use this form to have students apply your choice of science vocabulary words and to give them multiple opportunities to use the words in context. At the bottom of the page, you will find ideas for using the words (i.e., spelling tests, journal entries, oral interviews, etc.). Give students a new page each time you want them to practice a new set of science words.

◆ *So What Do You Want to Know in Science Today?* (page 81) Students can complete this open-ended activity as they work through a project or experiment. They can record their observations and questions directly on the page.

PROCESS SKILLS CHECKLIST

Student_____ Observation Period _____

Skill	Level of Competency		
	Novice	Competent	Expert
Observation			
Classification and Comparison			
Analyzing and Collecting Data			
Asking Critical Questions and Formulating Hypotheses			
Investigation and Measurement			
Communication of Findings (Written/Oral)			

LIFE SCIENCE CHECKLIST

Student_____ Observation Period _____

Knowledge Demonstrated	High (3)	Average (2)	Weak (1)
Identifies and describes major functions and systems of plants			
Identifies and describes major functions and systems of animals			
Classifies organisms in the plant kingdom			
Classifies organisms in the animal kingdom			
Describes how matter and energy are used in the plant kingdom			
Describes how matter and energy are used in the animal kingdom			
Explains the process of adaptation in both plants and animals			

GA-1671 Middle Grade Assessments

LIFE SCIENCE CHECKLIST II

Student_____   Observation Period _____

Skill	High (3)	Average (2)	Weak (1)
Explains how the food chain works			
Describes the function of genes and chromosomes			
Identifies the parts and functions of the human reproductive system			
Identifies the parts and functions of the systems of the human body			
Describes the role of food and nutrition in maintaining optimal body function			
Analyzes the relationship between the environment and human health			
Describes the dangers of drugs and alcohol to the human body			

EARTH SCIENCE CHECKLIST

Student_____ Observation Period_____

Knowledge Demonstrated	High (3)	Average (2)	Weak (1)
Weather systems and their impact on man and the environment			
Storms and storm prediction			
Maps and weather			
Climate and Earth			
The Solar System—Features and components			
Relationship of Earth to other galaxies, planets, systems			
Movement of celestial bodies			
Gravity and other space science concepts			

EARTH SCIENCE CHECKLIST II

Student_____   Observation Period _____

Skill	High (3)	Average (2)	Weak (1)
Concepts of erosion and soil conservation			
Types of soil and use in agriculture			
Oceans and oceanography			
Aquaculture and ocean medicines			
The fossil record and its uses			
Volcanoes, earthquakes, and plate tectonics			
Wind, water, ice and Earth			
Geologic pressures and geologic time			
Earth history			
Layers of Earth			

PHYSICAL SCIENCE CHECKLIST

Student_____   Observation Period _____

Skill	High (3)	Average (2)	Weak (1)
Describes physical and chemical properties			
Explains physical and chemical changes			
Lists and describes properties of matter and energy			
Understands structure of the atom and atomic energy			
Uses the periodic table of the elements for reference			
Understands heat, color, and light concepts			
Understands concepts of electricity			
Understands concepts of magnets			
Understands introduction to physics: time, velocity, friction, force, momentum, acceleration, kinetic energy			

ENVIRONMENTAL SCIENCE CHECKLIST

Student_____ Observation Period _____

Skill	High (3)	Average (2)	Weak (1)
Ecosystems			
Air and water pollution			
Conservation of natural resources			
Conservation and care of animal habitats			
Endangered species			
Plants as medicine			
Global changes and science			
Energy and resources			
Relationship of man to the environment			

3-POINT RUBRIC FOR A SCIENCE TASK

Student_____ Date _____

3 Points—Serious Scientist

- ◆ Demonstrates use of process skills with ease
- ◆ Uses equipment competently
- ◆ Documents and analyzes results in a neat and organized manner
- ◆ Shows strong curiosity and interest in the scientific process
- ◆ Uses science vocabulary in a fluent, knowledgeable manner
- ◆ Exercises leadership skills in group tasks
- ◆ Completes the project on or ahead of time and follows all steps
- ◆ Employs technology with ease and creativity

2 Points—Successful Scientist

- ◆ Demonstrates appropriate use of process skills
- ◆ Uses equipment with occasional assistance or direction
- ◆ Documents and analyzes results
- ◆ Shows curiosity and interest in the scientific process
- ◆ Uses science vocabulary with a minimum of error
- ◆ Works well with a group
- ◆ Completes the project on time
- ◆ Employs technology in an appropriate manner

1 Point—Seeking to Be a Scientist

- ◆ Demonstrates use of one or more process skills
- ◆ Requires assistance or supervision to use equipment
- ◆ Needs more practice in documenting and analyzing results
- ◆ Seldom shows curiosity or interest in science
- ◆ Seldom uses science vocabulary appropriately or with ease
- ◆ May demonstrate problems in working with a group
- ◆ Did not complete the project on time or by following directions
- ◆ Requires assistance in using technology appropriately

Your overall score is_____. Comments:_____

_____

_____

SCIENCE FAIR PROJECT EVALUATION

Student_____ Date _____

Title of Project _____

Grade Level _____ School _____ Science Teacher _____

◆◆ **Category:**   Life Science   Earth Science   Physical Science
                  Environmental Science   Psychology   Technology   Other

Evaluate the quality of each criteria and assign 1, 2, or 3 "beakers." A rating of one beaker describes an
Acceptable Project; 2 beakers is an Exemplary Project; and 3 beakers is a Superior Science Project.

Statement of Hypothesis
Comments:

_____

Quality of Abstract
Comments:

_____

Statement of Purpose
Comments:

_____

Description of Variables
Comments:

_____

Accuracy of Procedures
Comments:

_____

List of Materials
Comments:

_____

Data Collection and Analysis (Graphs)
Comments:

_____

Results and Conclusion
Comments:

_____

Organization and Presentation
Comments:

_____

SCIENCE VOCABULARY CHECKPOINT

Chapter _____ Theme _____

Terms and Definitions

1. _____
   _____

2. _____
   _____

3. _____
   _____

4. _____
   _____

5. _____
   _____

6. _____
   _____

7. _____
   _____

8. _____
   _____

Checkpoint:

Spelling Test _____ # Accurate _____

Used in Journal _____ # Accurate _____

Oral Interview _____ # Accurate _____

Other Assignment _____ # Accurate _____

Terms to Review:

_____

_____

_____

Name _____ Date _____

So What Do You Want to Know in Science Today?

• •

What do you want to know? _____

_____

What do you predict will happen? _____

_____

Can you illustrate your predictions here?

What materials will you use and how will you use them?_____

_____

These are the steps you used to find out:

1. _____   5. _____

2. _____   6. _____

3. _____   7. _____

4. _____   8. _____

Describe your results.

_____

_____

Illustrate your findings.

Was your prediction correct? _____

How might you change the variables next time?

_____

CHAPTER FIVE
ASSESSMENT IN FOREIGN LANGUAGE

INTRODUCTION

Something to Think About:
"We can do anything we want to if we stick to it long enough."
(Helen Keller)

Current research in brain science (cognitive science) suggests that windows of opportunity for learning a foreign language are open widest during the elementary school years, under age 12. In fact, the journal *Nature* now reports that a foreign language learned in the early years is stored in the same part of the brain as a child's native language. When a child is older, however, the new language pushes into other parts of the brain, looking for a home. With this powerful research in mind, middle schools are introducing more opportunities for foreign language.

Materials in Chapter Five and How to Use Them

Listed below are the pages contained in this chapter. Also listed are ways to use these pages.

◆ *Checklist for Foreign Language Progress* (page 83) Use this page to record student progress in any foreign language. There are both language and grammar skills on the checklist to track.

◆ *Rubric for a Foreign Language Project (Cultural)* (page 84) This teacher-directed page can be used in both foreign language classes and in other classes that study culture.

◆ *Foreign Language Progress Journal* (page 85) Give students many copies of this page. Have students place the pages in their individual notebooks to help them keep up with their own learning. Have students fill out this page at certain intervals (i.e., every two weeks).

◆ *Foreign Language Progress Postcard* (page 86) This "postcard" is designed to be sent home as a form of parent communication, just like a real postcard is used to communicate with friends and acquaintances.

CHECKLIST FOR FOREIGN LANGUAGE PROGRESS

Student _____   Observation Period _____

Language _____   Evaluator _____

Skill	Proficiency Level		
	Growing (1)	Competent (2)	Fluent (3)
Knowledge and usage of vocabulary			
Grammar and sentence structure			
Conversational skill			
Accent			
Spelling			
Reading and translation			
Knowledge of culture			

RUBRIC FOR A FOREIGN LANGUAGE PROJECT (CULTURAL)

Student/Team_____ Date _____

Brief Description of Project _____

_____

Culturally Connected—3 Points

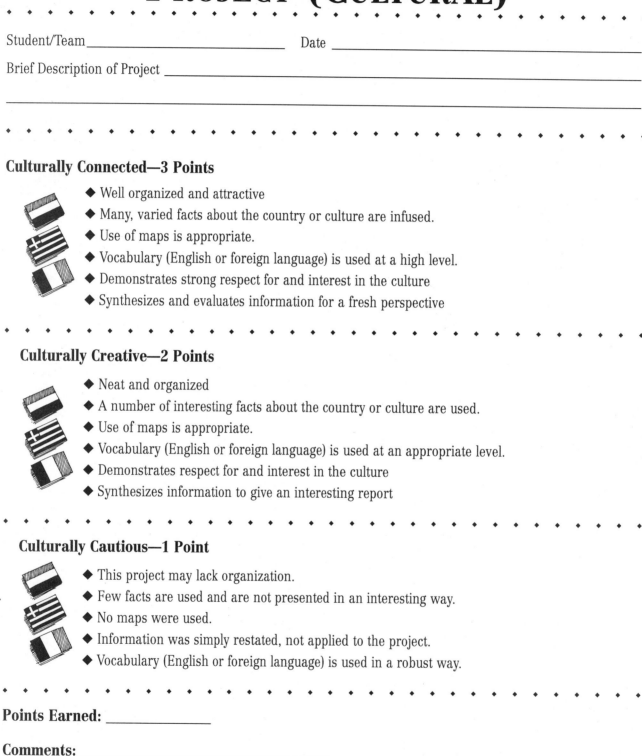

- ◆ Well organized and attractive
- ◆ Many, varied facts about the country or culture are infused.
- ◆ Use of maps is appropriate.
- ◆ Vocabulary (English or foreign language) is used at a high level.
- ◆ Demonstrates strong respect for and interest in the culture
- ◆ Synthesizes and evaluates information for a fresh perspective

Culturally Creative—2 Points

- ◆ Neat and organized
- ◆ A number of interesting facts about the country or culture are used.
- ◆ Use of maps is appropriate.
- ◆ Vocabulary (English or foreign language) is used at an appropriate level.
- ◆ Demonstrates respect for and interest in the culture
- ◆ Synthesizes information to give an interesting report

Culturally Cautious—1 Point

- ◆ This project may lack organization.
- ◆ Few facts are used and are not presented in an interesting way.
- ◆ No maps were used.
- ◆ Information was simply restated, not applied to the project.
- ◆ Vocabulary (English or foreign language) is used in a robust way.

Points Earned: _____

Comments:_____

_____

_____

Name _____ Date _____

FOREIGN LANGUAGE PROGRESS JOURNAL

Language _____

Today, I learned this new word: _____.

Today, I learned how to say _____.

Today, I learned this new fact about the culture: _____

_____

Today, I practiced my technique of _____

I am getting more proficient at _____.

My Foreign Language Diary

_____

_____

_____

_____

_____

_____

_____

_____

_____

_____

_____

_____

_____

_____

_____

_____

_____

_____

_____

FOREIGN LANGUAGE PROGRESS POSTCARD

Greetings from _____!

Your child _____ is making progress in learning the language. During this grading period, I would describe his or her progress as _____.

In the acquisition of vocabulary, he or she is _____.

The use of accent is _____ and his or her conversational ability is _____ _____ needs to continue to work in the area of _____

Be sure to _____ to do this. In the area of _____ his or her progress is especially strong, and this is something to be proud of! If you need to talk with me, please call _____.

Sincerely,

_____,
(signature)

CHAPTER SIX
ASSESSMENT OF SPECIAL TOPICS

CREATIVE ARTS ✦ SERVICE LEARNING ✦ PHYSICAL EDUCATION
ATTITUDE INVENTORY ✦ GENERIC CLASS CHECKLIST ✦ ORAL PRESENTATION

INTRODUCTION

Something to Think About:
"Well done is better than well said."
(Benjamin Franklin)

Materials in Chapter Six and How to Use Them

The checklists in this chapter are straight-forward and simple, but the content areas that they cover have typically been ignored by assessment. That is why this chapter is so unique and helpful. Below are descriptions of each checklist.

◆ *Creative Arts Checklist* (page 88) Use this in music, drama, chorus, or fine arts.

◆ *Service Learning Checklist* (page 89) Use this instrument in vocational education, tech-prep classes, or in any class that has a strand of service learning in the curriculum. Service learning is an important trend in education in which students prepare for the real world of work by engaging in service projects.

◆ *Physical Education Checklist* (page 90) Use this with any kind of sport or physical education program.

◆ *Student Attitude Inventory* (page 91) This can be helpful for guidance programs or for creating long-range plans that require a documentation of student interest.

◆ *Generic Class Checklist* (page 92) Are you keeping up with a skill? An attitude? Use this page to monitor whole class progress in any subject area.

◆ *Evaluation of an Oral Presentation* (page 93) This evaluation can be used in any subject area in which an oral presentation or report is given.

CREATIVE ARTS CHECKLIST

Check One: ____ Music ____ Drama ____ Dance ____ Chorus ____ Fine Arts

Student_____ Evaluation Period _____

Skills Demonstrated	Proficiency Level		
	Growing (1)	Progressing Well (2)	Mastery (3)
Technique			
Creativity			
Expression			
Commitment			
Use of equipment or materials			
Punctuality and professionalism			
Neatness and organizational skills			
Other			

GA-1671 Middle Grade Assessments

SERVICE LEARNING CHECKLIST

Student_____   Evaluation Period _____

Service Learning Project_____

_____

Abilities	Rating Scale			
	High Level (1)	Strong (2)	Growing (3)	Improvement Needed (4)
Organization and planning				
Timely completion of project				
Communication—oral/written				
Problem-solving skills				
Cooperation				
Professional dress and grooming				
Interest in service to the community				
Use of equipment and tools				

PHYSICAL EDUCATION CHECKLIST

Student_____ Evaluation Period _____

Skill or Game _____

Demonstrates sportsmanship   Yes   No
Comments:

Uses equipment appropriately   Yes   No
Comments:

Knows the rules and follows them   Yes   No
Comments:

Punctuality   Yes   No
Comments:

Attends class and dresses out   Yes   No
Comments:

Shows leadership ability   Yes   No
Comments:

Specific technique _____ Yes   No
Comments:

Specific technique _____ Yes   No
Comments:

STUDENT ATTITUDE INVENTORY

Student_____   Teacher _____

Grade _____   Date _____

Response 1: Most of the time, your attitude toward school seems to be

very positive.   positive.   ambivalent.   negative.

Response 2: Most of the time, your attitude toward completing work seems to be

focused and energetic.   interested but distracted.   negative.

Response 3: Most of the time, your attitude toward working with others seems to be

enthusiastic and friendly.   positive.   anxious.   angry.

Response 4: Most of the time, your attitude toward other students in class seems to be

respectful.   friendly.   distant.   unfriendly.   shy/anxious.

Response 5: Most of the time, your attitude toward teachers seems to be

respectful/courteous.   anxious/shy.   hostile/unfriendly.

Response 6: Most of the time, your work habits can be described as

organized.   good days and bad days.   chaotic and messy.

Comments: _____

_____

_____

_____

_____

_____

_____

_____

Generic Class Checklist

Subject _____ Period _____

Students	Skill	Check ✔	Minus −

EVALUATION OF AN ORAL PRESENTATION

Speaker _____ Topic _____ Date _____

Criteria	(Check the right box in matrix.)		
	Completely	**Adequately**	**Marginally**
This presentation fits the time limit set.			
A device was used to get the audience's attention. 　　Rhetorical question 　　Anecdote 　　Startling statistic 　　Visual aid 　　Music or media 　　Emotional impact			
The speaker maintained eye contact and used hand gestures where appropriate.			
Voice and tone inflections were effective.			
The presentation followed a logical sequence.			
Data and information were used to make a point.			
The speaker's point of view was clear.			
Appropriate visual aids were used.			
The presentation kept the audience's attention.			

CHAPTER SEVEN
DESIGNING YOUR OWN ASSESSMENT TOOLS

INTRODUCTION

Something to Think About:
"And I am right, and you are right, and all is right as right can be."
(Sir W.S. Gilbert)

◆◆

Although the instruments throughout this book are designed to be generic and open-ended, there are many reasons for designing your own evaluation tools. This chapter contains teacher-directed activities and models for making tests and authentic assessments that are valid and useful.

Materials in Chapter Seven and How to Use Them

Use pages 95–96 for creating and giving traditional tests. Pages 97–98 can be used for creating your own rubrics, which are meant for use in authentic assessment. Turn to pages 99–100 to find blank, ready-to-use forms on which to imprint your own criteria for rubrics.

If you like the more open-ended checklist model, turn to page 101. This page contains guidelines for making checklists.

The last page in this chapter, page 102, *Checkpoint for Teachers,* is perfect to use in a faculty or team meeting to help assess your strengths and weaknesses in making your own assessments. This kind of information may be helpful to you because less than 10% of teacher preparation programs require a course in testing and measurement, and teachers often feel a lack of confidence in their abilities to make good evaluation tools.

TEST-MAKING TIPS

In all things, seek balance. This is the number one tip for test-making and for assessment in general. Plan for a balance between traditional and authentic kinds of assessment in your middle grade classroom and you will probably do the following:

◆ Meet the assessment needs of students who display a variety of learning styles.

◆ Assure parents who display a variety of parenting styles that you know what you are doing.

◆ Find out a lot about how you teach.

◆ Find out quickly what the students have (or have not) learned.

◆ End up with a lot of information that will enable you to plan for meaningful instruction.

Keeping these points in mind, consider the guidelines below for structuring a "traditional test", your typical "end of the chapter" mathematics, science, or history assessment of content.

1. Review the content that you taught and make sure that that information only is on the test. Telling sixth-graders to "read the chapter" on their own is not only meaningless, it is a poor kind of instructional strategy. If you didn't go over it, give examples and demonstrations, review it, and put your heart and soul into it, then you didn't teach that content, and it shouldn't appear on the test.

2. Create a variety of test items and group them together. For example, design 5 or 6 multiple choice items and group them together. Do the same for short answer, matching, and fill in the blanks. This is called having a variety of "response options".

3. Be judicious about the use of "true or false" test items. Don't design them as a sadistic form of trickery. Instead, make the items clear, but if the student selects "false", he or she must give the "right answer". (Example: T or F—Syracuse is the capital of New York. Answer: False, Albany is the capital of New York.)

4. When you use the "multiple choice" response option, make sure that all of the "choices" are about the same length, or students will quickly figure out that the longest choice is most likely to be the correct one.

5. In the "multiple choice" option, keep your *distractors* appealing.

6. When using the "matching" response option, be sure to keep the items clustered around a common theme. (Example, names of famous African American inventors) Don't mix in a lot of other data. To keep thinking at a high level, throw in an "extra" item or two.

7. With "fill in the blank" response options, avoid using more than two blanks in a sentence. This keeps your validity high. Also, make the sentences short. You are assessing for content knowledge, not reading ability.

8. Be aware of "time" in the design of a test. If you are creating a test that has only short response kinds of items (no essay), then 2–3 pages of items can be done in a 45–60 minute period.

9. If you are including one or more essay items, then give at least 20 minutes of thinking and writing time for each item.

10. With essay items, consider offering a "choice" of 2–3 questions for students to respond to.

11. Mix "easy" and "harder" items in the test.

12. Consider dividing your test day into two parts: one for short item assessment and one for a longer "written" or "oral" assessment.

13. Consider giving a traditional "short item" test for part of your assessment and asking for a longer, more intense written or performance task as a second, "authentic" assignment. The grades can stand alone or be averaged together.

14. Select your test day with care. Avoid Fridays, Mondays, the day before a major holiday, the day after a major holiday, or the day of a big school or community "event", such as a soccer playoff or the tryouts for senior band.

15. Confer with other teachers on your team or grade level about when they are giving tests. Avoid scheduling major tests on the same day.

16. Prepare the test with care. Use large, bold print. Give ample room for written responses. Keep it long enough to be valid, but brief enough to assure reliability.

17. In regards to vocabulary words, spelling should count on a formal test.

18. Reread your directions to make sure that they are clear.

19. Let the students know on the test how many points each item is worth.

20. Avoid the words, "should, never, always, almost" in designing test items.

REALLY GOOD RUBRICS

For performance-based assessment, you need a rubric. A rubric, simply put, is a description of the range of student performance. You can have several levels of performance or just two to three. Right in the middle, you need an "average or acceptable" level and work above or below that to describe richer or poorer performance. It is that simple and that complex. Rubrics are tough because the teacher has to decide beforehand what is expected and what is possible. Some might advocate creating the rubric after the students do the work and then describe the range of performance. There are, however, many opponents to this way of thinking.

If you give out the rubric before the students work, students should know what is expected and what they can expect from your assessment of their work. Below are steps you can follow to design your own rubric:

1. Think about what you taught. Just like the traditional test, your rubric should only evaluate what was actually taught. That is what the students should be held accountable for.

2. The rubric should fit a range of student abilities. If your students are quite gifted, then the "average" performance should be a bit more rigorous than the "average" for a slower group. Likewise, the range above and below average should be fitting.

3. Decide on your "categories" or "ranking of performance". Below and on page 98 are some ideas:

◆ **Students Did Really Well**

Excellent

Above Average

Strong Performance

Outstanding Performance or Product

Exemplary

Superior Achievement

Gifted Performance

Complete Understanding

High Pass

Expert Level Performance

More Than Meets Requirements

◆ **Students Did Right**

Acceptable Performance

Commendable

Correct

Average Performance

Achieving Well

Adequate Understanding

Passing Performance Level

Meets Requirements

♦ **Students Need Work**

Limited Understanding

Incomplete Performance or Task

Needs Improvement

Revision Needed

Not Passing

Weak Performance

Needs Assistance

Novice Level Performance

Does Not Meet Requirements

Once the categories or rankings have been set, you can begin the process of "describing levels of performance" or "descriptors of criteria". Simply put, put your cards on the table. Tell the students (and parents) what your standards are. Be sure to match your standards to the district's scope and sequence and even national standards to assure a robust rubric.

Start by listing the facts and ideas and level of development that mark the "middle range", or acceptable, level of performance.

Then develop your criteria for the ranges above and below that average level. Ask yourself: "What would a really good one look like?" Ask yourself: "How will I know when a student has missed the mark?"

Decide how many rankings or ranges you want. Perhaps you will want just 1–2–3. Or, do you have a fairly complex task and need a range of 1–5 to adequately describe performance?

Determine the points or grade to fit the rankings or range.

Make sure that your rubric is valid—that is, that it measures what it is supposed to measure. If you are teaching in an interdisciplinary fashion, mixing language arts and social studies, then it makes sense for your rubric to include criteria for communication skills in the product. However, if the task didn't ask for written performance, then your rubric shouldn't evaluate it either.

On pages 99–100 are blank rubric forms you can use to help you design rubrics appropriate for your students.

3-POINT RUBRIC

Student_____   Date _____

Evaluator_____

◆　◆

_____
(Title)

Description of Performance   **Rankings of Performance**

_____

_____

_____

Points Earned: _____

Comments: _____

_____

_____

5-POINT RUBRIC

Student_____   Date _____

Evaluator_____

◆ ◆

_____
(Title)

Description of Performance   **Rankings of Performance**

Points Earned: _____

Comments: _____

_____

_____

GA-1671 Middle Grade Assessments

CREATING CHECKLISTS

Checklists differ from rubrics in that the teacher is observing and monitoring performance over time. The rubric is typically used to evaluate one product or performance, usually an important one. The checklist, on the other hand, is used to keep up with students' progress in a certain discipline or with their completion of specific tasks over a period of time. Checklists can cover a lot of area on one sheet of paper. If you leave room, one can even jot down helpful anecdotal evidence concerning the behaviors or work completed.

Basically, checklists have two parts: the listing part and the rating part.

The listing part can be used for the following:

◆ behaviors

◆ affective performance or attitudes

◆ work completed

◆ skills demonstrated

The items on the list can be rated as follows:

◆ pass/fail   or   ◆ yes/no   or   ◆ most of the time/often/seldom

However, a more fancy "scale" can be created and the items can be reviewed across a range, using numbers or descriptors.

CHECKPOINT FOR TEACHERS

RATE YOUR ASSESSMENT-DESIGN STRATEGIES

Assessment Validity	Circle Your Rating		
"Testing What You Taught" Notes to Me:	I'm Wonderful	I Can Do It	I Need to Do It Better
Assessment Timing Notes to Me:	I'm Wonderful	I Can Do It	I Need to Do It Better

Designing Test Items
   T/F
   Matching
   Short Answer
   Essay
   Fill in the blank
Notes to Me:
	I'm Wonderful	I Can Do It	I Need to Do It Better

Length of Test
   Too Long
   Too Brief
   Variety of Response Items
Notes to Me:
	I'm Wonderful	I Can Do It	I Need to Do It Better

Reviewing for the Test
   Every Test
   Every Time
   Thoroughly
   Provide an Outline
Notes to Me:
	I'm Wonderful	I Can Do It	I Need to Do It Better

APPENDIX

• •

Something to Think About:
"The reward for a thing well done is to have done it."
(Ralph Waldo Emerson)

Materials in the Appendix and How to Use Them

The materials provided in this appendix are provided to help you plan for and carry out meaningful assessment. Good teachers know that assessment cannot be separated from instruction nor from curriculum. (See the drawing below.)

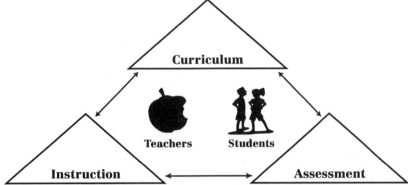

Therefore, the items located in the appendix will help you coordinate efforts between curriculum, instruction, and assessment. Start by reviewing the *Glossary of Assessment Terms* on pages 104–106. Knowing the meanings of assessment terms makes you both confident and prepared in creating or choosing the appropriate tools.

Two versions of *Parent Postcards* (pages 107–108) are offered for your use. Many school districts require teachers to provide their tools for parent communication as part of teacher evaluations. These postcards are wonderful and easy ways to keep communication between home and school open. Fill out and send these postcards home as often as possible. Keep parents informed of their children's progress. Assessment is not helpful if parents don't know about it. A report card is not enough. Parents need ongoing, consistent reports about their children's growth over time.

To help students monitor their own progress, the *Student Contract* (page 109) and the *Student Interest Inventory* (page 110) have been developed. Students must be actively engaged in their own learning and in the assessment of that learning. Again, many schools now require teachers to show that they have done this. These kinds of forms demonstrate your efforts to hold students accountable for assessment. Give these forms to students at certain times during the year. Have students keep the filled-out forms in their folders and refer to them as needed. Check students' progress by comparing the forms from different observation periods.

Finally, with a movement toward reflective teaching, which is, in itself, a form of assessment, the final two items in the book are offered. The *Team Planning Questions* (page 111) and the *Time Out for Reflection* (page 112) are for you to use in groups or by yourself. Assessment is only going to be as good as your intentions. How do you really feel about your own teaching? How does your middle school team view assessment? What commitments will you and your team members make to assessment? This kind of inquiry is expected from today's educators, and *Middle Grade Assessments* delivers the tools to help you express that inquiry.

GLOSSARY OF ASSESSMENT TERMS

achievement: the amount of knowledge or skill that the student has mastered

affective: refers to the non-cognitive or non-intellectual domain of values, feelings, emotions, interests, and attitudes

anecdotal record: a document used to record brief observations about student performance or behavior over time

authentic assessment: the use of meaningful, real-life tasks and problems to evaluate a student's progress and skills

authentic instruction: the use of non-traditional methods to engage students in cognitive and creative activities that lead to in-depth knowledge

authentic learning: the learning that occurs when a student can independently or collaboratively apply knowledge to solve problems or to produce knowledge in an original way

benchmark: the results of an assessment used to mark a student's level of achievement at a particular point in time

bias: an assessment risk that occurs when the format or content of an evaluation tool deliberately or accidentally places one group (social, ethnic, racial, gender) at an advantage over others

Bloom's taxonomy: a taxonomy developed by Dr. Benjamin Bloom that describes cognition at six levels—knowledge, comprehension, application, analysis, synthesis, and evaluation

checklist: a simple form of assessment in which teachers and/or students use a list of behaviors or skills to keep track of individual or class performance

coaching: pairing students of differing ability levels and/or multiple intelligences to assist and support one another in solving problems and completing tasks

cognition: the process of acquiring new knowledge and using previous knowledge in unique ways; thinking

collaboration: the art and science of working with others to solve a problem by drawing on the individual skills and talents of group members

constructivist: one who embraces the belief that students create knowledge by using what they already know to make sense of new experiences and materials

convergent question: a test item that has only one correct answer; also known as a closed question

criteria: specific behaviors or descriptors used to score student's work

criterion-referenced test: a traditional test in which the student must solve a predetermined number of items correctly in order to meet a standard; The emphasis is on mastery of items.

curriculum: all of the skills, objectives, goals, resources, materials, and plans used in the process of schooling